Beautiful Dreamer

December '95

To Tom & Revi Bell & family
  Merry Christmas!
  Happy New Year!
  Best wishes
From Ceres So Alabado

(This includes some notes on your Lolo Sal
  & J. Antonio Araneta, historical now)

Beautiful Dreamer

Ceres S.C. Alabado

Sulu
Books
San Francisco

Library of Congress Cataloging-in-Publication Data
Alabado, Ceres S. C.
Beautiful Dreamer / Ceres S. C. Alabado
ISBN 1-887764-51-8
95-074903 CIP

Manufactured in the United States of America
The Text is set in 12/16 Garamond
Design by Brian Romero
First Edition

ACKNOWLEDGEMENT

I wish to acknowledge the invaluable help of the gracious and efficient librarians of the public libraries of Sunnyvale, Santa Clara, San Jose and Daly City in Northern California, in the United States; the National Historical Institute (NHI) and the National Library in the Philippines, in locating and supplying the reading materials/documents I needed to check out my historical data, and for the reprints of the historical photographs. My deep gratitude to my daughter-in-law Baby Dulce Alabado who sent me the historical photos of the destruction of Manila which she painstakingly reproduced from copies at the NHI and the National Library.

I wish to thank readers of my manuscript for their suggestions and comments: Corazon S. Vigilia, retired teacher of the FIlipino Education Center in San Francisco; Gemma Nemenzo of the *Filipinas* magazine; Helen Mendoza, University of the Philippines professor of English. Thanks, too, to my friends for communicating with me their recollections of "those days": Purita de Vera Roa, one of the Rinkydinks of our high school days at the Philippine Women's University; Behn Cervantes of *Special Edition* magazine in New York and his sister Rachel in Florida; Loging and Zenith Arguelles in New Jersey.

To Rhea Beth Ross, my instructor at the Institute of Children's Literature in Connecticut, for inspiring me to pursue this writing project and its publication; and to the indefatigable Eduardo Datangel, Brian Romero, Bong Velasquez, Karen Singson, and Carl Angel for the painting used on the cover, my heartfelt gratitude.

This book would never have been printed without the absolute support of my husband Corban, and our children, Arion and Dulce, Alan and Mildred, Ariel and Carol, Ana and Tomas Segovia, Arrigo and Ma. Theresa.

Dedication

in memory of

Dr. Gervasio and Jacinta Santos Cuyugan

and

Rev. Victoriano and Emilia Alabado

and to all

The Defenders of the Philippines,

the Filipino people.

Introduction

Introduction

The Philippine Islands were invaded and colonized by Spain in 1521. More than three hundred years later, in 1896, the Philippine Revolution almost succeeded in throwing off the the yoke of Spanish rule over the Islands until the Spanish-American war broke out and Spain sold the Philippines to America for $20 million. Thus at the turn of the century, America came to "own" the Philippines: the first American involvement in South East Asia.

The Filipinos, frustrated in their desire for freedom, fought the Americans in 1898-1900. But Filipino bolos were no match against American firepower, and soon the Filipino natives were "pacified" with the promise that the Americans would grant them independence in the future.

To prepare them for self-rule, America offered scholarships at American schools to deserving young Filipinos representing different regions of the country.

Gervasio Santos Cuyugan was one such *pensionado* (scholar) who passed a gruelling arithmetic and English grammar test. Young Gervasio had never had any formal schooling. He spoke the native Kapampangan and some Spanish, but not English. How did he manage to pass the test?

During the Revolution, he was *cobrador de jueteng* (collector of gambling bets) — a job that taught him the science of computing fractions of monies of the bettors. He was a messenger of letters and documents of the revolutionaries who taught him the rudiments of reading and writing and imbued him with the first stirrings of nationalism. Later, an American teacher, named Hyde Clinton, befriended him and gave him lessons in the English language, including the parsing of sentences. It was also Mr. Clinton who encouraged him to take the competitive test to possibly win the scholarship and advance his learning so he could best serve his country.

i

He sailed for America in 1905 at the age of fifteen, finished high school in California and went on to Chicago where he enrolled for a medical course at the University of Illinois, specializing in general surgery.

Upon graduation Gervasio returned to the Philippines and served in the government under the Bureau of Health. His first assignment was not as a surgeon but as a doctor collecting all those afflicted with Hansen's disease from every nook and corner of the country and bringing them to the leper colony in the isolated island of Palawan. Gervasio also taught the rural folks in the countryside the proper hygiene and sanitation in their homes and surroundings, and primary health care to prevent disease. Later he joined the faculty of the University of the Philippines College of Medicine and the Department of Surgery of the Philippine General Hospital.

It was at the Hospital where he met Jacinta Belza a coy, and shy girl from the Bicol province, and a student at the School of Nursing. In Bicol, Jacinta had been crowned Miss Bicolandia during the inter-provincial athletic meet. But for the young girl, beauty and titles were mere decorations to flaunt. She wanted more than that. So she left her hometown for the city and took up nursing. Dr. Gervasio fell in love with her. After a whirlwind courtship, they got married and raised a family in a home near Philippine General Hospital in Manila.

Dr. Gervasio Santos Cuyugan and Jacinta Belza became Papa and Mama — Pa and Ma.

This is the story of Pa and Ma and the family they raised in peace-time and in war. This story has been constructed from the following sources: the recollections of Mario, Ceres, Ruben, and Fides; family diaries and notes of Pa and Ma; and documents and books in the National Historical Institute and National Library in the Philippines and the public libraries of Sunnyvale, Santa Clara, and Daly City, California, USA.

Part I
1926 — 1932

" One thing I know: the only ones among you who will really be happy are those who will have sought and found how to serve"
— *Dr. Albert Schweitzer*

New Home

"H ome, Ma?" Ceres asked as the old silver Essex rumbled to a stop. She straightened up in her mother's lap.

"Yes, dear , here we are in our new home," answered her mother with a sigh of relief. "Wake up, Dar, Mario," she whispered into the ears of her two other children.

"Yehey-y-y-y!" shouted Mario and Dar as their father opened the car door, and out into the street the two boys jumped. Their little sister Ceres held fast to her mother's arms.

The Santos Cuyugan family had travelled a long way from Manila to Lucena. It had been hectic getting themselves and all their things together into the car. Now it was all over. Now they were home again in a new one.

"Pa, do you think that is our new house?" asked Dar, rubbing his eyes and looking up to a galvanized tin-roofed, wooden bungalow with an acacia tree towering over it.

Pa laughed. "Of course, it is. And it is going to be our home from now on," he said.

In Manila they had had a house too. A cream-painted, iron grilled cottage near the Philippine General Hospital where Pa worked, right in the heart of the city.

"I'm a doctor, a surgeon, and I work in a hospital," Pa had explained to the children.

Now Pa had come to organize and establish the provincial hospital in the capital town of Lucena in the province of Tayabas, south of Manila. He had explained this to the family. At first when he was asked to transfer, he hesitated. It meant moving out of the city, selling their house there, giving up old friends, and coming to live in a small strange town. It meant being strangers in that town. The only thing he knew about Lucena was that it was sorely in need of a provincial hospital. He, of all the doctors in the General Hospital, was chosen to do something about that. That was the way to look at it, Pa said.

And as for Ma, it had not been too easy to convince her either. She had been a nurse at the hospital before she was "Ma." And she knew when work had to be done. Still, it had been heartbreaking to see their house and all their furniture go, especially the piano. Ma loved music, and it was one of her joys to sit down before the piano and play as she sang "Beautiful Dreamer" and all the songs she knew.

"I'll get you another piano in Lucena," Pa assured her, "if it's the first and only furniture we'll get over there."

And so here they were.

In no time at all Ma and Pa had brought in all their bundled belongings from the car. Mario and Dar brought in the pillows and blankets. Ceres carried her little doll. She was only three years old and not expected to help much yet. Mario, the eldest, was six; Dar was four and a half.

The parcels were scattered in the different rooms. The suitcases, pillows, blankets, mattresses, and mats were in the three bedrooms. The boxes containing the kitchen utensils and dinnerware were in the kitchen, some in the dining room. Brooms and rags were on the floor of the living room. The house was an old one, stripped bare of furniture.

"We'll get some furniture, don't worry," Ma said when the children complained. "But first let's get lunch ready."

Pa searched inside the boxes for the one-burner electric stove.

"Emergency cooker," he called it. He set it up right on the kitchen floor next to where he found an electric outlet. The children picked can after can from the assorted canned goods they brought.

"This one, Ma, this one. Sardines, sardines!" chose Dar.

"No, no, this, beans, beans!" chose Mario.

"Me, this, this!" joined in Ceres.

"Ah, that's milk!" Mario said, laughing.

Ma had some sliced fresh onions and garlic already frying and sizzling in the pan. The spicy smell and smoke filled the warm room.

Just then Pa heard a gentle knock. The back door was slightly open. Pa pointed to the front door which was closed. "It's from here," he whispered as he tiptoed to the door and opened it.

There stood a fat, stooped, dwarfish, white-haired woman. She was all smiles, but toothless.

"Good-day to you all. Tecla is my name, Tecla Dimasupil. I'm your neighbor. I live back of this house. Is there anything I can do to help?" She spoke rapidly in Tagalog, the native dialect.

So unexpected was her appearance everybody just stood still and stared at her for a full minute. Pa opened the door wider to let her in.

"Yes, yes, if you please. Ma, what do you say?" Pa asked.

Ma couldn't have been more pleased. She did need a hand. She nodded and smiled.

"Let me then," said Tecla, waddling off to the side of Ma squatting on the floor beside the cooker.

Mario, Dar, and Ceres gathered around her. Mario thought she was the weirdest creature he had ever seen. Dar wondered where in the world she had come from.

"She's a witch," whispered Dar to Mario.

"Hi, hi, hi, hi!" Tecla laughed, not quite minding them.

"Who are you?" Dar asked her at last.

"Tecla, I told you," the witch answered. "Please speak Tagalog. I no speak the English."

"Do you live here?" asked Mario.

"No. I told you, I'm your neighbor."

"Where's your house?" asked Dar.

"Out there." She pouted and thrust out her lips, pointing to the back of the house.

Mario and Dar looked out of the back window.

"Where? There's nothing out there — only the acacia tree," said Dar.

"Later, I'll show you. First your own home. You haven't seen all of it yet, you know."

"We have, we have!" the children chorused.

"Have you seen that little cupboard up there?" She pointed with her lips to a cupboard on the wall. "You'll see the biggest spider web in there. That's because no one for years has bothered to destroy it."

The children were all ears and silent.

"Have you seen the fuzzy little nest of the old silly maya birds underneath the roof over there?" Again she pointed with her lips, as she laid out the dishes on a tablecloth spread on the floor.

The children shook their heads.

"Have you seen the *salagubang* and *salaginto* bugs — hundreds of them — in those acacia trees? Shake the branches; they'll drop down — tog! on your heads."

The children giggled.

"Have you seen what quacks — tucko! tucko!" She puffed her cheeks and punched each side with her fist to make the quacking tucko sound. "Up somewhere in the ceiling. You'll hear it tonight!"

The children opened their mouths wide.

"See, you haven't seen anything of your new home. First things first." She chuckled as she called out, "Lunch is ready!"

Ma and Pa came out of the bedroom. Tecla whispered to the children. "Eat first. After lunch, I'll show you."

Tecla

Tecla was only the first of the family's callers. Day after day many other neighbors came to offer friendship. One of them, Patro Unson, a piano teacher, came to advise Ma on the purchase of a piano. As Pa promised, the piano was one of the first pieces of furniture acquired for the house. Ma said she could not be without one for a long time. The Cervantes family came too. Rosario Cervantes was a mestiza American-Spanish while Ma was a Filipina-Spanish. "That's one thing we have in common," they joked each other. "We're both mestizas."

All the doctors and nurses who were going to work in the hospital came too, in groups. They got acquainted with each other before buckling down to work together. They discussed the question of the building. It has been selected, they told Pa.

"All washed up clean, Doctor, before you came. I saw to it," said Miss Allarey who was going to be the chief nurse.

Someone said the operating room had a brand-new operating table. A week before, reported Doctor Queblar who was going to be the resident-physician, truckloads of beds and beddings were sent in from the city. "Everything was shaping up," said Doctor Villasenor, the assistant director.

"Then what else am I going to do?" joked Pa.

Pa and Ma met many more of the townspeople. So many strange names and faces, but all the people seemed friendly and affectionate.

Still, Tecla was the family's favorite. Not because she was the first to have come to their house. Not because she was fat and joyous and lively, always on hand to help. Sometimes they did not see her for days. When they began missing her, there she was again with her toothless smile. Something endeared her to the family. She was like sunshine after a rainy day.

She washed their clothes, swept the yard, cooked, made sweetmeats, and dusted the furniture, for soon the family also bought tables, chairs, and beds. She showed the children the huge spider web in the cupboard. Not only that, but the spider himself. He was black as charcoal with white stripes on the legs. Ma had ordered the cupboard cleaned out; and the poor weaver had to move out, house and all.

"When we came here, we didn't have to tear down our house," wailed Dar.

"But you sold it, that's the same," declared Tecla.

She showed them the tucko — a gecko, an enormous lizard-like reptile that brought good luck to the house if you didn't stone it away. And so they didn't. She taught them how to shake the branches of trees for beetles — one shake for salagubang, two for salaginto. She brought the nest of the maya birds down from its perch while Mario and Dar held a ladder steady at its foot, and then she brought it back up because those silly birds would chatter all day looking for their home, she said. She did all that. She opened up the heart of the house to the children.

But mostly she washed. She became the family's washerwoman. Ma paid her a few pesos.

"Aba, but I'm not asking you to pay me," she protested.

"I didn't say you did, but I want to pay you," said Ma.

There was something else about Tecla. She had a home, back there in the woods. Where it was exactly, she kept putting off telling them.

"In the woods?" Dar asked.

"What woods?" Ceres asked.

"Where's the woods?" Mario asked.

"Oh, you silly city people! Imagine asking me all that. As if I can tell you. Hi, hi, hi, hi!" Tecla laughed.

"But you're old ..." insisted Dar.

"So what!" exclaimed Tecla.

"You know," said Mario.

"The old do not know all the answers to your questions, my dear, remember that," Tecla said. "But I promise to take you there, one day. Someday."

Then one day, as Tecla rocked little Ceres on her lap, she hummed a little tune. First it was just a gentle hum. Then her lips filled up with words.

> *Singkuling my little girl*
> *Upon my lap, upon my chair*
> *Singkuling my little girl*
> *In my nipa hut, in the deep, deep woods...*

Ceres remembered the promise. "You'll show us that? In woods?" she asked.

Tecla did not answer. She kept humming the tune. She kept singing the words, *"Singkuling my little girl..."*

Ceres listened carefully. Later she told Ma. Ma was peeling Batangas oranges and feeding peeled sections to all of her children. She was like Mother Bird dropping worms into the beaks of her little ones. Ceres danced and skipped around and around her, while chewing the juicy fruit. When she got in front of Ma, she opened her mouth wide for the orange. Mario and Dar just sat still to the left and

7

right of Ma, waiting for their turns. It was a mid-morning ritual Ma observed as punctual as the clock. Ma said orange was good for their teeth.

"Yes, Ma, Tecla said she's going to take us there, someday," Mario confirmed the report.

"A nipa hut in the woods! My, that's interesting," said Ma. "We have nipa huts, too, in my hometown but I did not live in one."

Just then Tecla came up from the back stairs.

"What's up, Tecla?" Ma asked her. "Is it true you live in the woods. Outside town?"

"Ay — no, no,no, Ma'am. Ay — yes, Ma'am," she answered uncertainly. "Just back of this house, Ma'am."

"Back of here? Why, I never realized there was anything like that back of this house," said Ma.

"Yes, Ma'am, there is. There is always something back of anything, Ma'am. If you come with me, you'll see."

Nipa Hut in the Woods

⚜

Pa and Ma could not come along. Pa was busy in the new hospital. Next time he would, he said, but he could not promise. Ma had to do the cooking at home. She would come, too, some other time. Only the children would go.

"I-can-hardly-wait-to-get-there," said Mario, with his mouth full of hard-boiled egg and bread.

"Shhh — don't talk when your mouth's full," scolded Ma.

"You, Ma, can be?" asked Ceres.

"No, not even me. I wait till I've chewed and swallowed my food before I talk," answered Ma.

Over in the kitchen, Tecla was packing a small rattan basket with sandwiches and fresh oranges. It was eight o'clock in the morning.

"At ten be sure you eat those oranges," Ma ordered. She told the children to behave. She told them to be back soon.

They were on their way. The warm early morning sun peeped through thin layers of white clouds.

"It's going to be a fine morning," Tecla said happily. She whistled; "Singkuling my little girl ..." Oh joyful whistling, Ceres thought. But

Ma had said ladies and little girls should not whistle, especially when in company with others. Then she wondered why Tecla did it. Tecla had no teeth. But Ceres kept silent. Let her, let her, everything was joyful. Mario and Dar were silent, too.

They were taking in everything. They were walking down a path after having crossed the street behind their backyard. They walked in single file on the narrow path. Tecla leading the way, Ceres and Dar following, Mario at the rear. The footpath cut through a wide grassy flat ground, dotted with unmoving carabaos here and there, whose heads slanted down low to the ground.

Suddenly, Mario skirted out of the path into the grass, and like a little lizard, slowly crept up to one of the carabaos. The carabao's skin was covered with cracked, dried-up mud. He looked up to Mario. Mario backed up a step. The carabao walked two heavy steps away and bent down. He began to munch grass vigorously, with a crunching sound.

"Mario, come back here!" shouted Tecla.

"Ah, he's eating grass," observed Mario.

"Yes, and he can eat you too, so come back here!" Tecla called again.

"Really? Can he eat me?" asked Mario.

"Well, if he doesn't like you, he'll bite you," said Tecla.

Mario ran back to the path. They all trudged on again. Little brown maya birds darted across in the sunlit air above their heads. Twittering, they flew on ahead leading them toward a grove of trees. First, there were a few guava trees. The mayas alighted on these. Then, there were clumps of tall thorny bamboos, their leafy tops bowing in all directions. As they passed them, Mario noticed that Tecla bent down by the stumps and seemed to be whispering, then to be picking up something.

"What's that?" asked Mario.

"Mushroom," whispered Tecla.

"Why are you whispering?" asked Mario.

"Shh, don't you see that little rise over there?" and Tecla pointed with her lips to a mound among the bamboo stumps. "That's the *punso* of the *nuno*. The nuno lives there. We must say 'Excuse me.'"

"*Nuno?*" Mario, Dar, and Ceres chorused.

"Shh, not too loud. Don't you know? He's a dwarf. We must hurry or we'll never get away from here." Tecla tiptoed back to the path, in her hands a pile of fresh mushrooms.

The children followed her, still thinking about the *nuno sa punso*. And about the mushrooms.

When they were a good 10 meters away from the bamboos, Dar asked, "What will you do with those mushrooms, Tecla?"

"Stupid! You should ask, 'will you eat 'em?'" Mario said.

Tecla did not say anything. She could not tell the children she was so poor she and her daughter, for she had a daughter, ate nothing but these mushrooms from the bamboo stumps. Besides, they would not understand her, she thought, because they had so much on their table, so much to eat. They were very rich. What could they understand of poorness? But she had always been poor. Her husband had been a coconut-tree fruit climber until one day, because he was drunk, he fell from the tree on his head and died. Tecla and her daughter became poorer and poorer.

Yet Tecla never once complained of her lot. What's the use, she said to herself. She was strong and she could work. And later, when her daughter grew bigger, she too would work, not go to school. What was the use of school, if they had nothing to eat, she would tell her child. She went from house to house in town seeking work. But it was hard to find work even in a friendly town when one was a widow with a child. And so Tecla left her child back home in their little hut among the coconut trees, while she continued her search for work. It was then she came upon the family who had just arrived from the big city of Manila. Surely, she thought, they were rich, they were city people.

"Is it far yet, Tecla?" Dar asked.

"I'm tired," complained Ceres.

"Come, let me carry you," offered Tecla, kneeling down on the ground. "Hop on my back, hug me tight." Ceres promptly jumped piggy-back on Tecla.

"We're going just a little beyond the big river we're coming to. Do you hear it?" asked Tecla.

The children tried to listen. They did not know the sound of a river in the woods, how could they tell if they heard it?

Suddenly, there was this great gurgling sound as if a giant was washing his mouth with water. But they could not see it yet. They were crossing through neat rows and rows of coconut trees, many of them laden with clusters of round green nuts. The children looked up occasionally to the great tops of the trees where the nuts were.

"Are these coconuts all yours, Tecla?" asked Mario.

"Oh no, no, no, hi, hi, hi, hi!" laughed Tecla. "If they were, I'd be rich. They belong to a rich man. We, we squat at the very edge of this plantation, me and my daughter. I have a daughter, you know. I didn't tell you. She's the one who calls this the 'woods.'

"Here, here's the river now, see? And this is the edge of the coconut plantation. After this, nobody owns the land. So we put our house there. There, can you see it?" She pointed to it with her lips, there, across the deep gorge.

Mario, Dar, and Ceres did not follow where she was pointing at. Nor what she was explaining to them, for already their eyes were feasting on the mighty flowing river.

"Oh, can't we go down to the river?" asked Mario.

"And wet our feet?" added Dar.

"No, no, that's very deep. First, you'll have to learn to swim. Not now. Come." Tecla called. "Here's the way to cross it."

Tecla, with Ceres on her back, disappeared among some thick undergrowth and emerged a few feet lower from where the boys stood.

"Follow me," ordered Tecla.

12

Mario and Dar followed the trail. Then they saw Tecla and Ceres waiting for them at the foot of a monkey bridge.

"Oh, it's hanging over the river!" exclaimed Dar.

"No, it's not, stupid!" said Mario. "Look, it's sitting on the high ground."

Indeed each end of the long platform sat on the hard grassy ledge high above the river. The bridge was made of four very long bamboo poles fastened side by side together with sturdy rattan strips, forming a platform to provide a way across. Higher up, intertwined vine ropes tied to acacia trees on both banks of the river, above the span of the bridge, served as a handrail.

"Now be careful," Tecla warned them. "No giggling and pushing. Just walk slowly. Hold on to the vine above you. Like this."

Once again Tecla, loaded with Ceres, led the way. She was an expert at this. She could do this even with her eyes shut. They moved slowly, ever so slowly. One after the other. No one talked. No one laughed. No one looked here and there. Just straight ahead. Until Tecla at last embraced the trunk of the tree on the grassy ledge at the end of the bridge. Mario and Dar, one after the other, did the same. Then Tecla led the way up again, climbing to the level ground above the bridge.

At last they saw Tecla's little nipa hut in the woods.

"Just like in the pictures," said Mario.

Indeed it was a nipa-thatched hut on stilts of long posts stuck on the ground, with a ladder leading to a doorway. The roof was thatched, the walls and windows were patches of wooden boxes and woven sawali palm and coconut fronds. Tecla knelt on the ground to put down Ceres.

From the hut, a little girl, the size of Ceres, rushed out to greet Tecla. She paused in her tracks when she saw the others. Slowly she approached Tecla, touched Tecla's hand to her forehead, to greet her, "*Mano po.*"

"This is Deling, my daughter. She's as old as you, Ceres," said

Tecla. And to Deling, she said, "These are Mario, Dar, and Ceres. 'Member? I've told you about them." Then she handed over to Deling the bunch of mushrooms.

Tecla urged the children to climb up the bamboo ladder into the hut. The children scrambled up, the ladder squeaking with each of their little steps.

"Our hut's nothing but this, but you're welcome, you can come here anytime your mother lets you. Now let's fill up with our food."

Tecla squatted on the bamboo-slatted floor as she passed around the sandwiches and oranges. So hungry and thirsty were they, including Deling.

"Now let's play," said Ceres. "I want to play."

They were still munching their sandwiches when they rushed down the ladder into the grassy ground. The sun was just above their heads, on the tips of the coconut fronds.

"What?" asked Dar.

"Follow the leader," said Mario. "Do you know that, Deling?"

Deling smiled shyly and shook her head no.

"Do you know pat-a-cake?" asked Dar.

Again Deling shook her head.

"Ball, do you have a ball?" asked Mario.

Deling shook her head once more.

Ceres was at a loss. Mario and Dar shrugged.

Then Deling said, "*Luksung tinik* (jump over the thorns)."

"What's that?" asked Ceres. "Teach me."

Deling took the hand of Ceres and together they sat down on the grass face to face, their legs bent at their knees, their feet touching each other on the toes. Then Deling told the boys to jump over and across their knees.

Mario and Dar jumped one after another, easily.

Then Deling stretched her right arm and told Ceres to stretch hers too, so they could touch each other with their hands upright one on top of the other, fingers all spread out wide apart, Ceres' little finger touching the thumb of her other hand, while Deling's little finger touched the tip of Ceres' thumb, thus making a fence of thorns.

"Now jump over this," Deling challenged the boys.

Mario jumped first. He made it quite easily.

Dar jumped and fell face down on the ground. He didn't cry. He laughed. "That's too high," he complained.

"Now our turn," said Ceres.

The boys sat on the ground and made the hurdle, first with their knees. The girls easily leaped over this. Then they made the finger-hurdle, fingers spread out straight up, little finger on top of the thumb, hand on top of the other, for the girls to leap over the thorns. Whoops! the girls didn't make it. They fell flat on the ground, their skirts caught on the thorns.

"One more time, one more time," said Ceres. "I can do it."

"We have to go," called Tecla from the hut. "Your ma said be back soon."

"No, one more time," insisted Ceres. She pulled up her skirt, jumped, and made it.

Christmas

eling and Ceres became fast friends. Tecla brought Deling to town one day for a visit with Ceres. After that, Deling would often tag along with her mother. When she didn't, Ceres looked for her. Tecla would then have to promise that Deling would come the next day. Sometimes it was Ceres, with Mario and Dar, who went to visit Deling in the hut in the woods. They would play *luksung tinik* and other games they taught each other or invented. They played *piko*. They hopped about on a figure of a house drawn on the ground. They played *tatsing*. Standing about two meters away from a one-foot square drawn on the ground, they would each throw a flattened stone into the square. They played *buga*. First they would gather cashew fruits from the scattered cashew trees that occasionally grew among the coconut trees, bite off the meaty flesh, then spit out the kidney-shaped nut to hit the other player's nut. They played hide-and-seek, flitting here and there among the trees like dragonflies and cockroaches.

Ma had let them go out into the woods as often as they wanted.

She herself had gone with them sometimes. "Oh, it's like my hometown Buhi," she had said. "There we have the mountains and the lake instead of the river."

It was only Pa who had not been to the woods with them. Pa was too busy at the hospital.

"And besides," Pa told the children, "I've been to all the woods and towns of the country when I was a young man, you know. It was my dream then after I had seen the poor unsanitary conditions of our people all over the country, to change them. After coming from a country like America where many homes had proper tap water and toilets, why, I had to compare ours here. And imagine me sitting elbow to elbow in the same banca boat with leper patients, their faces and limbs deformed, touching mine . . . no nose, no hands." He paused. So as not to alarm the children, with a wink of his eye, he added: "There were not too many sick people then. I had to go look for them high up in the mountains, in the deep, deep woods."

And so the days, weeks, and months passed quickly.

Soon it was going to be Christmas. But it was the "just before -Christmas" time that made it the most exciting season of the year. What made it better was that Pa and Ma who were always busy attending conferences with grown-ups or parties with town officials, or doing such things the children did not participate in, were for this occasion part of it all. They made themselves part of all the plans and preparations. They made Christmas a day with a very special meaning for the family.

Especially for the children. A day for sharing and playing with all the children of the neighborhood. Playing Santa Claus to all these children. Here in Lucena, as it had been in Manila, it would be no different, Ma said.

The exciting preparations began. Ma sent out written notes to all the little children, rich and poor, mostly poor, around the neighborhood, including the disabled children at the hospital who were to be allowed to go out just for the day. Next, she took a quick trip to Manila and back, to buy the assorted "gifts" of little toys and fruits, pencils and crayons, and picture books to be packed in paper bags for each child.

Everyone in the house, from Pa to little Ceres, helped pack the paper bags. There were so many of them, they took the whole of three days to finish. When the bags were all filled up they stood upright in rows in the living room.

"My, that's a lot of kids," exclaimed Pa when the last bag was counted.

"Close to five hundred," Ma said.

"Wow!" cried Dar.

"Where'll we put them?" asked Mario.

"The bags? Or the children?" asked Ma.

"The children," replied Mario, "when they come."

"The world is as big as one's heart," said Pa.

"As our home," Dar continued. "That's what Ma says."

"As our backyard. We'll have the pageant there too," said Pa.

As always there was going to be a pageant of the nativity of the Christ Child on the eve of Christmas. It was planned to be set up in the backyard. Pa was in charge of that. He asked a hospital nurse to be the Virgin Mary. Pa chose her because she had a smiling face. "And she has a big stomach," he added, laughing.

The hospital's assistant director was St. Joseph. The little girl-doll of Ceres was the Christ Child who was a boy. It did not matter, Ma said. A baby could be a girl or a boy, it looked just the same in the manger. Mario and Dar and other big children were shepherds. Ceres and Deling were little angels. Three hospital attendants were the three kings — Gaspar, Melchor, and Balthazar.

"Everyone knows the story of the birth of Jesus. No need for rehearsals," said Pa. "Only the costumes are to be prepared ahead of time. Each one take care of what to wear. The king's costumes and the angels' wings are the most elaborate. They need more attention than the ordinary poor people's clothes of the Virgin Mary, St. Joseph, the baby, and the shepherds, the baby most of all ..."

So Ma and Tecla sewed the long-caped gowns of Gaspar, Melchor, and Balthazar, from bedsheets they dyed purple, red, and blue. They pasted fluffy cotton on cardboard "wings" for the angels. Pa cut out the cardboard "crowns." All around these crowns, in different designs, Mario and Dar pasted pieces of torn rags Tecla had given them. Ceres and Deling collected a basketful of fallen, dried, cone-shaped little brown coconuts in the woods. With Ma, they painted the nuts with brilliant crayons in reds, greens, and blues. Later Pa bore holes through them and strung them together to form the letters CHRIST CHILD hung over the manger.

The manger was a milk carton box, which Tecla stuffed with hay from the fields. A black carabao borrowed from a farmer and washed clean of mud with the garden hose was tied to the acacia tree. The piano was moved close to the kitchen facing the backyard. For a star, Tecla bought a star-shaped *papel de japon* paper lantern from the market. With an electric bulb inserted inside, the lantern was suspended on a wire just above the letters CHRIST CHILD. At night, lighted up, it was a real shining heavenly star in the darkness of the yard.

Last to be set up was the Christmas tree. Every year Pa thought of a different one. It might be a pine tree from Baguio or just a plain leaf-bare tree with branches painted white or covered with fluff of cotton or soaked with soap suds left to dry, or hung with "icicles" of strips and curlicues of aluminum tin foil. This year it was a bamboo tree. Mario had suggested it, remembering the one they often saw in the fields, how its tip bowed in just the right way. With decorations left over from the past years — little paper and tinkling metal bells, tiny plaster Santa Clauses, red and fat life-like, rubber dolls and animals, beads and heart-shaped colored bulbs to wind around and around the branches' edges — everyone had a hand in dressing up the forlorn tree. Ma attached the strings to each decoration. From Ma each little piece was taken by Ceres and Deling, turned over to Mario and Dar, and handed up to Pa and Tecla who stood on wooden stools, the better to reach the topmost branches.

At last it was the eve of Christmas.

Mario could hardly wait for the day to end so "Christmas" could begin. Dar kept asking Ma if it was time to put on the tattered shirt and trousers of the "shepherds."

"I like to be poor, I like to be a poor shepherd," Dar insisted. "So I will see Jesus when he's born."

Ceres and Deling were all over the living room, the kitchen, the yard. They counted and counted the bags. They pulled down the "icicles" and hung them back curled over the branches. They tasted the sweetmeats in the kitchen — the *ube*, the *macapuno*, and milk pastillas candies.

Then Tecla said it was time to be ready for the pageant. Mario, Dar, Ceres, and Deling rushed to the bedroom where all the costumes had been laid out on the bed. The kings and other shepherds, St. Joseph and Virgin Mary, were all fussing over their clothes.

Soon the first guests arrived. Little children with big sister or brother, or mother, or father, or all together. Or just many children holding hands afraid to let go of each other. Most of them were barefooted. All of them were wide-eyed. All of them were open-mouthed with wonder. At first they came in slowly, reluctantly, through the open gate. At first they hid behind big sister, big brother, mother, or father. At first they hid behind each other, each pushing the other forward. Forward. Up the stairs. Through the porch. The living room. The kitchen. Then down the back stairs, to the yard. All over the yard. Now they were all over the house and the yard.

Pa as usual was the bearded, fat-bellied Santa Claus. He stood by the Christmas tree letting each child pick up his or her paper bag. Amidst the squealing, joyful laughter, chatter, and scurrying feet, he bellowed:

"One each! One each! Or there'll be none left for the others.

Hala, one for each only! If I catch you cheating, I'll hang you up the tree!"

Then he saw one little boy eyeing another bag after he already clutched one of his own. "Aha, you want to be hung up the tree, eh?" Pa said.

The little boy nodded, his eyes brightening.

"Okay, you can have another one — that's the last , hah?" And Pa laughed.

Night was setting in when Ma played the first notes of "Silent Night, Holy Night" on the piano. Everybody quieted down. Everybody listened to the opening notes. They sang softly, tenderly:

> *Silent night, holy night*
> *All is calm, all is bright*
> *Round yon Virgin Mother and Child*
> *Holy Infant so tender and mild*
> *Sleep in heavenly peace, sleep in heavenly peace.*

The lantern shone brightly. Around the manger where lay the Babe Jesus, the Virgin Mother Mary, St. Joseph, and the shepherds stood watch. Above them, standing on stools, the two little angels.

Then Ma played "Hark, the Herald Angels Sing" while the three kings glided sedately down the back stairs, across the yard through the crowd, to the manger. There, one after the other, the kings offered gifts of myrrh, frankincense, and gold to the little Babe Jesus in swaddling clothes.

At this point, Ma struck up "Joy to the World" and all joined the singing again. The Christmas tree lights in the living room blinked and twinkled. The full moon and the million stars in the dark sky brightened as the night glowed and deepened. The whole earth received her King with gladness.

Pa with the aid of a flashlight read the words in the Bible:

"... And Jesus said: Except ye become as little children, ye shall not enter the kingdom of heaven ... And whosoever shall receive one such child in my name receiveth me..."

Quietly each child went forward, one by one, and stood before the manger, lingered there a while, then turned away into the darkness. It was Christmas.

At midnight, the church bells in town rang. Pa and Ma had seen off the last of the little guests and now they hustled up the whole household for the Mass in the big church in town. The night had grown colder. They put on flannel sweaters and shawls.

All Lucena came to the church for the final song to the newborn Babe. After Mass everyone greeted each other by the church door, in the patio, in the street, *Maligayang Pasko, Maligayang Pasko*, Merry Christmas, Merry Christmas!

"I can't wait to see what Santa Claus brought me for Christmas," said Mario.

"Me too," said Dar.

Ceres and Deling were too sleepy to care much about their Christmas gifts.

Hospital

Sometimes Pa did not use the car. He walked to the hospital and back. The hospital was just across the park in front of their house.

Mario, Dar, and Ceres often walked with him but only up to the park. Next to the woods they loved to explore the park's secrets, the concrete man-made caves and passages in the unusual irregularly-built bandstand, the huge rock gardens where Cupid pee-ed into the mouths of frogs or the petals of gumamela flowers. When they got tired of exploring, they raced to the playground where they first tried the swings, then the see-saws, the slides, the merry-go-round, then back to the swings, until they heard Ma call them from the house for the orange "feeding."

A few times, they walked on with Pa to the hospital garden where Pa let them climb the big aratiles tree. "Be good, and take care of your little sister." Pa would kiss them as they parted. He to the hospital, they to their tree. They forgot all about the oranges at home, waiting for them. For there, up in their favorite tree, there were those juicy red aratiles, just waiting to be picked. These were little soft, round berries, sweeter and juicier than Ma's Batangas oranges. Ma knew it was useless to call. She would just wait till Pa brought them back home with him.

It was one of those days the children decided to go with Pa to the hospital. As they were crossing the street from the park, a car whizzed by, screeched to a stop, then backed up in front of Pa. Pa held back the children.

A woman jumped out of the car. Embracing Pa, she cried,

"Doctor, Doctor, have mercy, have mercy. Please look at him. He was stabbed, stabbed. Save him! Oh, please save him! Next to God, you are our savior. Save him!"

Pa looked into the car. Mario and Dar stood on their toes and looked in too. Ceres was too short to be able to reach up to the window, even on tiptoe. She could not see what Pa, Mario, and Dar saw: A man lying on the back seat, blood oozing out of his stomach.

"Come, quick, to the hospital!" ordered Pa.

The car turned around the curve to the entrance. Pa, Mario, and Dar walked as fast as they could. Ceres had to run as she kept asking, "What's it, what's it, hah?"

Nobody answered her. Pa was silent. He seemed to have forgotten the children were with him. As soon as he reached the steps that led up to the entrance door he scampered up. He did not kiss them, "Be good." They stood there, not knowing what to do.

"What's it, what's it, hah?" Ceres asked again and again.

"A dead man with blood in his stomach. I saw him," Dar boasted.

"Let's follow Pa," Mario suggested.

"He'll get angry. He says there's so many germs in there, we'll get sick," Dar warned them.

"Let's just go to the aratiles then," said Mario.

The hospital garden was a wide strip of lawn that hugged the squarish two-story building all around it. Shrubs and shrubs of gumamela and rosal flowers, and in between aratiles and aguho trees decorated the lawn. But there was one big fruit bearing aratiles somewhere at the back. This was the children's favorite. The rest of the trees were too small yet to carry their weight. Or if already strong and big enough, they had no special attraction. They bore no juicy aratiles berries. What was the use of climbing them, they had better stick to their favorite, they said to each other. But now a bright idea struck them all at once, as if by common consent of their minds.

"Let's try the other aratiles tees," they chorused.

"Maybe we can see from up there what's going on inside there," said Mario, pointing to the glass windows of the hospital.

Each climbed a different tree. Ceres managed to get halfway up a young trembling fruitless one. "I can't," she cried. "I'm afraid."

Mario was far out. What he could see was almost the rooftop. "I can't see anything," he complained.

Dar chose the tall slender one leaning against a corner window of the building. Perched on one sturdy branch at the level of the open window, he could lean farther forward to see through the iron grills. His eyes opened wider and wider. He didn't dare talk. Nurses and doctors it seemed, and others in long loose white gowns were bending over what looked like a sheet-covered table in the middle of the room. Hanging from the ceiling, just above their heads, was a huge blinding light. What were they doing, he wondered. Was Pa one of the doctors? He couldn't tell. Quickly he stepped down branch after branch to announce his discovery to the others.

"I saw it! I saw it!" he shouted, as soon as he touched ground. The two joined him where he stood beside the tree. "There, up there, in that room. There's a bright light shining on a table. And the doctors and nurses — with covered hands and heads and mouths — they're not talking. I don't know what they're doing," he said breathlessly.

Mario lost no time in climbing up and seeing for himself. Ceres could not climb that high. She just waited down below for relayed news.

"Yes, they're operating. That's Pa operating in the stomach of that man in the car. I know it's Pa. His hands have gloves, this long," and he let go of the trunk on which he leaned, and pointed almost up to his elbow.

"Let me see again, let me see again," insisted Dar. He climbed up once more.

The two took turns on that sturdy branch. They were afraid the branch could not carry them both. After one had gone down, the other climbed up. One up, the other down. Ceres got tired waiting down below. She would no longer be left out, she said to herself. She insisted on her turn. Her two brothers said she could not, that she would fall. But she ignored them and slowly inched her way up. When Mario and Dar realized that she was so hard-headed and determined to make it, they at last agreed to help her in every possible way they could. Mario climbed a branch ahead of her and pulled her hand while Dar pushed her buttocks. Then she went up on her own. Once more they pushed her up. At last she was there on that sturdy branch. She was on top of the world, it seemed to her, watching Pa "operate."

But she wasn't there one minute when the boys started pulling her down. "My turn, my turn," said Dar.

Dar saw Pa hold out his gloved hand. A nurse handed him something that looked like a sharp knife. Next Pa seemed to have begged for something again. A pair of scissors. He was motionless for a long, long time. But Dar could see round beads of perspiration forming on the bridge of his nose, which was uncovered. Everyone stood by, unmoving too. Like statues in the park, thought Dar. Pa bent down low, lower and lower, so low. He looked so small because he was really a short man. The other doctors looked down over his head. And then he straightened up, head bent somewhat backward. But his eyes, sharper than ever, were looking down at his work.

"My turn, my turn." This time it was Mario insisting to climb up again.

The doctors and nurses now moved about more often, then more briskly. At last the room was quite empty. The bright light went out. Mario climbed down fast. "It's over, it's over," he announced.

It was some time before Pa came out, calling them. It was time to go home. They joined him at the edge of the lawn. Together they crossed the street.

The hot noonday sun had eaten up all their shadows on the street. In the park. Pa was silent. The children were too tired and hot to say anything. They walked side by side with Pa, faster and faster to keep up with his hurried steps. Pa looked back and saw that

Ceres trailed far behind, so he waited for her, picked her up and carried her in his arms. Ceres was thinking about her having stood there in that topmost branch and her having seen Pa "operate." Yes, Pa was a surgeon. She remembered when Dar asked what a surgeon did and Mario answered that he cut up people.

"He cuts off the appendix," Mario added.

Then Dar had asked, "What's the appendix?"

It was Pa who answered, "Why, that's an extra — what'll I call it — tail of our large intestine. It has no important function there, but it could give you trouble if it gets busted."

"Then why does God put it there?" Dar had insisted on knowing.

"To show you that even small and useless things can give you trouble — can kill — so you have to watch out for even the littlest thing or happening in your life. It may mean your life or death." Pa always answered their questions thoroughly, even though he knew they only half understood him. He always talked to them, "lectured" to them, Mario said, as if they were grown-ups.

"Pa, I saw you operate." Ceres could not keep her thoughts to herself any longer.

"I know, I know." Pa finally broke his silence. "Next time I'll put you three on stools in the operating room. So you can watch me operate, not in that branch where you may fall off. Because if you do, I'll have to operate on you too. You, Ceres, will be on the highest stool. Or else, I'll put all of you on the operating table and cut you up." Ceres giggled.

"Gee, that was a very difficult operation. So you saw me, hah?" said Pa. "But I think I'll save that man. Imagine all his intestines and stomach hanging out of his body, all cut up. It'll be a miracle if he lives." He fell silent again. The children too. They were too tired to talk.

When they reached home, they saw an old man sitting in the front porch. Pa immediately recognized him. He had been his patient some two weeks ago. At his feet lay two live chickens tied together.

"Now, now, what's this, what's this all about?" Pa roared.

Ma rushed out through the front door. "Nothing, Pa, he came to thank you for his operation. He brought these," and she pointed to the chickens on the floor.

"No, no, no, go, go!" cried Pa. "Go on home with your chickens, you need them more than I. I told you, you don't have to pay me."

"The doctor's tired." Ma apologized to the caller. "You will have to excuse him. It isn't always he refuses kindness like that."

The old man picked up his two chickens and hobbled down the stairway. He was too embarrassed to say a word.

Again Ceres remembered what she saw at the hospital. Pa, in his white long gown, sweat trickling down from his forehead to his mask-covered nose and mouth, his powerful gloved hands gently moving with shiny steel instruments, while everyone in the room clustered around him, eyes riveted on him or at what he was doing. She wondered what Pa was so angry about now. Perhaps Ma was right. Pa was tired.

Tecla put the children under the shower and then gave them lunch.

"You know what?" she said gaily. "There's only one thing about your pa, hah! He cares nothing about anything but to give."

An Angel in Heaven

Ma first noticed it. Dar was running a mild temperature and he was not breathing normally. She put him to bed, gave him a quick sponge bath and orange juice to drink.

"Let Dar get some rest. Play quietly," she admonished Mario and Ceres.

When Pa came home from the hospital in the afternoon, Dar was expelling air noisily from his lungs, a hoarse brassy cough. Pa looked at his throat.

"Say a-a-a-ah!" He ordered Dar to open his mouth while he held down the boy's tongue with a wooden spatula, and flashed a pin light down to see his throat.

Pa shook his head. He looked worried. "I'll have to take him to the hospital," he told Ma. "Keep the children home."

"What is it? Tell me, Pa. Is it serious?" Ma wanted to know.

"It doesn't look too good. I'm not sure. I'll have to take more tests," Pa said.

"What does it look like? Tell me," Ma insisted She had been a nurse and she knew when a child's illness was serious.

29

"Diphtheria," said Pa uncertainly.

"Oh my God," was all she could say. Ma knew what diphtheria was. It was a dreaded highly infectious disease for which no known cure or immunization had been found.

Pa bundled up Dar and brought him to the hospital in the car. In the hospital, Pa put Dar in isolation right away. He ordered more tests to determine for sure the nature of his son's illness. Dar's pulse beats were becoming thready and rapid. Worse of all, he was having more and more difficulty breathing and swallowing. The worst of Pa's fears were finally confirmed. Dar had diphtheria.

Pa called up Ma at home, ordered that their whole household be quarantined to prevent further spreading of the infection to other homes. "No one must come in or out of the house," he said.

Pa carried Dar upright in his arms to help ease his breathing. Dar was listless but he wasn't crying.

"Pa," Dar's breathing was so labored his voice could hardly be heard. "Pa, I like it when I'm sick."

"Why?" asked Pa, barely above a whisper.

"Because you carry me," said Dar. Then he asked, "Will I get well? Am I — going — back home?"

"I don't know, Dar, let's pray you will. Ma and your brother and sister are praying too," said Pa.

"Will you operate me?"

Pa shook his head.

"Why not?"

Pa tried to find the right words to explain to his little son that not all diseases were curable by operation.

"What you have, diphtheria, it's not the kind of sickness that can be cured by operation, dear. I wish it were, so you'll get well."

"Will I— die?"

"Only God knows that, when He wants you to be with Him in heaven. Like the angels."

Then Dar coughed and coughed. Pa had to prop him up higher over his shoulder. He thought this posture helped open up his chest for more air.

For two days and nights Pa hardly put him down to bed.

Sometimes for a few minutes, Pa would sit in a rocking chair he had ordered placed in the hospital room, still holding Dar upright in his arms. Then he would walk around the room as if to gather more air for Dar to breathe.

On the third day, Pa himself seemed in a daze, so tired and exhausted was he. But he was still standing carrying Dar up in his arms.

"By and by, God will carry me," murmured Dar very softly, almost inaudibly.

Pa did not say anything. He kept rocking and rocking to and fro as if he was putting a baby to sleep. It was then a nurse on duty came up to him.

"Doctor, you may put him down now," she said in a softly shaky voice.

Pa was devastated. For a long time he sat on the rocking chair in hollow silence. Just staring at nothing. When he got up he stumbled on his way out of the hospital to the car. He could hardly find his way back home as he drove his car alone. Ma was in bed when he came in, speechless, followed by Mario and Ceres.

"Ma, we are out of luck," was all he could say, shaking his head.

Ma burst into a scream, a loud melancholy cry. Dar had not come home with Pa in the car. Ceres could not understand why Ma was crying hysterically. She had never seen her like that before. But she could not ask her why. Pa told her and her brother Mario.

"Go and kiss your Ma. Dar is not coming home to us. He is now with the angels in heaven."

For days, weeks, and months, all the nurses and doctors and attendants in the hospital, all the friends and relatives of the Santos Cuyugans from Buhi, Camarines Sur, and from San Fernando, Pampanga, sent sympathy letters and cards or came to their house to console the family in their time of bereavement.

Ma was inconsolable. She could not look at Dar's photographs, clothes, toys, books and things, without crying. It was as if she was going out of her mind. She would talk about him endlessly — recall all that he had said and done, reviewing them all in her mind: When he slipped from the wooden box he was standing on to reach the faucet while washing his hands and fell, plop! right inside the empty wooden box that had overturned; again, when Dar saw the water boiling in the pot on the stove and he called out in Ma's native Buhi-tongue, "It's *kalakalakaga*, Ma!"; and once when cry-baby Ceres howled with such an anguished cry that brought Ma to the scene, and she asked Dar because he seemed to have been the culprit, what it was he did to her, he had answered, "She asked for a box, so I boxed her!" How Ma laughed and laughed bringing all this back to memory.

Sometimes it seemed she had nothing more to live for and she said she wished for God to take her too.

Tecla would come to her, she was all over her. "No, Ma'am, I dunno who said it, it's not how far you fall but how high you bounce. Me, I fall many times, very bad fall, but I am poor, I have to keep busy to live. I scratch the sadness and hurt out of my day. Yes, Ma'am. There are coconuts up in the tree. But I have to climb and make them fall, " she chattered endlessly while offering Ma a drink or biscuits to eat.

Ma smiled.

Another time when Ma had that faraway look again, Tecla said: "Ma'am, you had Dar for six glorious years. Just think of it. Thank the Lord. And look at all your friends and relatives, Mario, and Ceres, and what's coming — big family, Ma'am."

"You have to be strong," Dr. Queblar, the resident physician said to Ma.

"You have other children to take care of," said Miss Allarey, the chief nurse.

"You have given back Dar to the Giver of life. Dar means to give, right?" said Dr. Villaseñor, the assistant director.

"And now you're going to have another baby," said Patro Unson, the piano teacher.

Ma tried. She tried very hard to think of Dar in heaven, and then of the baby that was coming.

"We'll name him Dar too, if he's a boy. Ruben Dario," said Pa.

School

"Ma, Ruben Dar cannot come with me to school!" Ceres declared as she was getting ready for the first day at school.

School was a nursery-kindergarten run by their neighbors Mr. and Mrs. Magill in their home. The Magills were American Christian missionaries who had been in the Philippines since American occupation in early 1900.

"No, child, of course not," said Ma. "Ruben's still a baby."

Ruben Dar was born a roly-poly baby, with facial features like Dar. It was not long after his birth that Ma had begun to believe the baby was indeed a reincarnation of her dead son, Dar, now an angel in heaven. As she nursed Ruben, she would sometimes point out to Pa how very much like Dar the baby was. God surely had a plan made out for everyone, for everything, she had said. One only had to discern it, accept it, and make decisions according to God's will. And God's will was for the good of all, she knew, even if she could not understand it, so harsh and unjust it seemed sometimes.

"Hah, you're not going to school," teased Mario. "That's not a

33

school. That's the home of Mrs. Magill."

"Never mind," replied Ceres. "Ma said it's Garden School. You, your school, does it have a name?"

"Of course. It's called Lucena Elementary School."

"Now, now, you two," Pa intervened. "Don't fight. You're both correct. Mario's in school in Grade III now, and Ceres is going to school in kindergarten. Now hurry, Ceres, Ma will walk you to school. I'll drive Mario to his school in the car."

Mario had gone to this kindergarten school, too. But then he had thought it was just playing in the neighbor's house. The Magills' school was a veritable magic garden for all little children. So it was for Ceres. As soon as she stepped into the garden, she was at once fascinated by everything there was to see and do.

There was a playground, like the park's but with more swings, slides, climbing ropes and bars, merry-go-rounds that you could ride to your heart's delight. There was one room, jutting out of the main house, that was screened all around and on top. It had trees growing right inside it and hundreds of yellow canary birds — mama, papa, and baby canaries — flying here and there, from tree branch to tree branch, chattering and singing such lovely melodies all day long. The kindergarten children loved to watch them. Mrs. Magill allowed them to go inside the room, two at a time.

"*Pay-dro*," called Mrs. Magill to her houseboy. "*Pina- kay-en-muna bay an mana aybon*? (Have you fed the birds?)" she asked.

Pedro rushed in from the kitchen with a bagful of birdseeds and a pitcher of water to pour into little cups inside the room. The birds, still singing their never-ending trills, crowded happily around the wooden cups for their meal and drink.

"Oh, oh, oh, look, they're hungry and thirsty!" shouted the children.

There was a little pond in the backyard with gold fish   swimming and hiding under big lotus leaves. Pedro dropped bread flakes into the water and the fish all came up to nibble at   the tiny crumbs.

There were all kinds of blocks of wood — building blocks of all shapes and sizes children could build castles and locomotive trains with, blocks with alphabet letters or numbers painted on them, or small spelled-out words written on them. There were little picture books of stories of the Bible, nursery rhymes, and coloring books.

After two hours of play and learning, the children were ready to be picked up. Ma came for Ceres. In the afternoon, Pa picked up Mario in the public elementary school some blocks away from home. Everything went well for Ceres' first day in school. For her, everything was magic in the fantasyland of the Magill home. She had fun.

But the next day, it was different.

Ceres wore a fancy blue silk dress with matching light blue socks and black shoes. Ma walked her next door to the Magills'. This time Ceres looked at the other children. She looked at the other girls. They were all about her size. But this time she noticed something. They did not wear anything like the fancy silk dress she wore. They did not have socks and shoes on. She looked at herself. She wanted to go home.

But Ma had left. After talking with Mrs. Magill, Ma had rushed back home. Ceres looked around and suddenly wondered why her friend Deling was not there. Why? Wasn't she going to school too? Didn't Tecla bring her to school? She felt lost. She could not understand why she looked so unlike the others. When she and Deling played together they both wore old clothes, no different from each other. And they said they would go to school together. At Christmas time they and the other children were angels or shepherds. Ceres knew she was just like all of them. Just a little girl like all of them. Why did she look different now? They were all staring at her.

What could she do? She began to cry. At first softly. Then loud and shrilly. Mrs. Magill came to take her by her hand and lead her to a chair. Instead of following, Ceres wrung off her hand and sprinted back to her house.

"I don't want to go to school. I don't want those girls. I don't want my new dress, socks, shoes," she cried.

Ma heard her. She came running from the kitchen to confront her.

"But why? What happened, Ceres?" she asked, taken aback by what she saw.

Ceres took off her new dress and threw it on the floor. She took off each of her shoes and kicked them on the floor. She took off her socks and rubbed them vigorously on the floor.

"I don't want a new dress, socks, and shoes," she cried, kicking them on the floor. "I don't want to be different. I want to be the same as they. No socks, no shoes, old dress." She was as nasty and adamant as could be.

Ma picked her up and sat her on her lap.

"Now you listen. Listen to me. You're not showing anything, acting that way, but your tantrums. Let me tell you something." When Ceres quieted down a bit, Ma continued. "I'll tell you a story of my mother, your Lola, when she was a little girl like you. She had a round whitish face, hair that curled down to the very tip. Folks teased that she was the child of the man in the moon, so white and bright was she. All the other girls in town were not like her. They had brown skin, straight black hair. They had broken teeth and sores all over their feet. They were different from her. Whenever she called them to play with her, they did not come. When she went near any of them, they turned their backs at her and left her. They whispered ill about her behind her back. They said she was the child of the man in the moon, a white Spaniard. They did not ask her to join them in their games. But Lola remained as she was. Of course she too wished she could be like them. She wished she could be brown and have ugly teeth and sores on her feet. Alas, she could not change herself. She could not throw off her face, her hair, her feet. But she wanted very much to play with the other girls. The other girls could not change either. They could not make themselves look like her. But they so wanted to play with her. At last, they decided they might as well let her play with them. And so Lola and the other little girls did not mind how they looked. They forgot that one looked different from the other. They just played together happily.

"Now you, Ceres, it is so easy for you to change your new dress and put on an old one — if that's what you want — to look like the others. For Lola, it was not that easy. She could not do that, to be not different." Ma paused.

Ceres listened intently but she could not quite understand Ma's long story. "What about Deling? Why wasn't she in school?" she asked.

"Oh Deling, about Deling," Ma said. "I tried to convince her ma, Tecla, to send her to school with you, you know. But Tecla said no, she needs her to work with her in their hut in the woods. I offered to take care of school expenses, but Tecla would hear nothing of it. She is so proud. Besides, she said, schooling, learning is a joke, and she laughed, 'hi, hi,hi, hi!' you know that cackling laughter of hers, and said, 'she will only learn English and go to America, hi, hi, hi,no, no, no!' Then she sang her little song, you know, the singkuling my little girl . . . life is sweet without a care. That's how she answered me. There's nothing I can do now. But I'll keep trying, Ceres. Is that all right with you?"

Ceres nodded.

"And think of Mrs. Magill," Ma continued. "She talks our language differently too, with a foreign accent. Didn't you notice? Because she is American, not Filipino. But who cares? Why do you want to not be different?"

Ceres had stopped crying. But she could not answer Ma. She did not know why she wanted to be like all the rest of the other girls. To be one of them, not set apart.

Pa as a student of the college of Medicine, University of Illinois, loved to play tennis at Lincoln Park, Chicago, USA taken in 1909

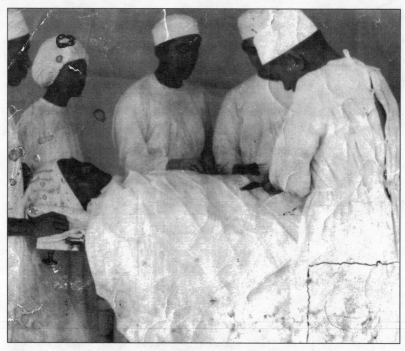

Pa head bent, operating on a patient in Lucena, Tayabas
(now Quezon Province) in the Philippines

Ma, second from left, as a nurse at the Philippine General Hospital
in Manila, the Philippines

Part II
1933 — 1939

Pilipinas kong minumutya
Pugad ng luha ko't dalita
Aking adhika:
Makita kang sakdal laya!
                    — Jose Corazon de Jesus
                        (Huseng Batute)

My beloved Philippines
Land of my tears and poverty
My fervent desire:
To see you completely free at last!
                    —tr. *by csca*

Typhoon

There's a typhoon signal up. No school today, kids," Pa announced after breakfast.

"Yehey-y-y-y!" shouted Mario, Ceres, and little Ruben who was now in kindergarten.

"Tecla, you and Deling, better stay here for tonight. You never can tell about these winds and your little hut. Besides, I'm due any moment now. I'd like you please to stay with the kids while I'm at the hospital," Ma said.

"Yes, Ma'am, we'll be right here," said Tecla.

Outside there was no stir of wind. No birds twittered in the acacia tree. Black clouds that had gathered fast overhead moments ago now stood still.

Ceres was happy classes were suspended. She was now in Grade III in the public elementary school where Mario was in Grade VI. She wore old dresses, not the going-out ones. And she wore slippers, not shoes and socks. So she was almost like the other girls. But something still bothered her. Pa always picked her up from school in the car. She was so shamed by this "special privilege" because all her classmates rode in dilapidated horse-drawn *calesa* or walked, no matter how far away they lived. Whenever Ceres got into the car, she would crouch as low as she could behind the front seat so as not to be seen by her schoolmates. "Pa, how embarrassing, I told you not to fetch me by car — can't you see, I don't like it! I don't like it!" she whispered. Pa said he needed the car for emergencies, in case he was called at any time in the hospital, not to show off. Ceres had to struggle hard with this thought.

Now, what was it that Ma said to Tecla?

"Ma, you're going to the hospital?" Ceres asked.

"Yes, dear, to have this baby here," and Ma pointed to her tummy. "Ruben is not a baby anymore. A baby sister? Or another brother? Which do you think?"

"Baby sister," Ceres answered.

"That's right," Pa said. "And we'll call her Fides. That's a good name. To be different."

"Why do you want us to be different, Pa?" asked Ceres.

" 'Cause you're special, my dear. Don't you want to be special?" Pa hugged her tight, gently. Ceres nodded. She wanted to be special to Pa.

The front door banged. The wind blew and forced the acacia treetop to sway to one side. The clouds overturned and raced across the sky. The rains poured down on the roof, on the window panes, on the wind-blown, torn, and battered leaves. Sometimes the rains sounded like the faraway train coming to a stop at the railroad station next to the park. The winds howled and whirled. And then they whistled and whistled as if calling other companion winds from somewhere out in the milky vastness. Sometimes it seemed they were so strong they were lifting the roof up from the house. At three o'clock in the afternoon, it was so dark, like night setting in.

Pa turned on the lights in the living room. It was safe and cozy there. The children sat and listened to the whistling rain and howling wind. Ma and Tecla were in the kitchen preparing an early supper. Then the lights went off. Pa warned the children.

"Now, kids, no running around. Just keep still. I'll go get some candlesticks to light up." He stood up to feel and find his way to the kitchen.

"Pa," Ma called softly. "I'm afraid we have to go."

Pa knew at once what she meant. He had been waiting for this moment. Although he had wished it would not come at this time, now that it had come, he braced himself for the task that had to be done. He picked up three candlesticks, gave two to Tecla and one to Mario.

"Light it up in the living room," he ordered his son. "And you all stay there while Ma and I drive out to the hospital, you understand?"

Pa backed up the Essex to park it right in front of the porch. He helped Ma down the stairs to the car, all the while holding a half-opened umbrella over her head and wrapping a thick overcoat around her. Just as he was driving away, he heard the old acacia tree crack up and then he saw it fall violently to one side.

"Look, Ma!" he shouted.

"Thank God, it fell on that side, not on our house," said Ma.

They did not look back to see the children rushing out into the porch to grieve over the fallen tree. It was not much of a tree lying there now. Its bare branches looked like mere sticks stuck to its trunk, but still swaying and swaying with the wind. Pa hurried away. Ma was in real pain.

It was midnight when at last Pa got home again. Howling winds still swirled and whistled driving the rain in all directions. Mario, Ceres, Ruben, Tecla, and Deling huddled cozily in the living room. Only one candle flickered in the dark.

Pa tiptoed to his room, his clothes soaking wet. "Pa, where's Ma?" Ceres' sleepy voice could hardly be heard above the din of the pounding rain.

"In the hospital, Dear, with your baby sister Fides." Pa smiled. "They'll be coming home soon. Like when she came home when Ruben was born — in two or three days."

"Pa, when Dar died, you said he became an angel and went to heaven. I was not sad, Pa. And Ma was not sad anymore when she had a baby, Ruben. A baby and an angel — are they the same?" asked Ceres.

"Yes, a baby is an angel — the most wonderful thing in the world, makes you not think of sad things. God makes it that way."

"God makes baby and angel?"

"Yes, God makes me and Ma make it happen. "

"God makes you make it happen," Ceres repeated.

Torch Parade

*I*t's here! It's here!" Mario shouted.

Ceres, Ruben, Tecla, and Deling, all rushed out to the porch where Mario stood on watch. While Pa held the car door open, Ma was coming out, a bundle in her arms. Ma was coming home with the new baby, the fifth in the family and the last she said she would have.

Everybody in the household had looked forward to this homecoming. After breakfast, Tecla, Ceres, and Deling went out into the fields back of the house to gather little *sampagita* and *adelfa* flowers for Ma and the baby. They waited all morning, all afternoon. Now the sun had set and they could barely see through the subdued light, Ma and Pa coming up the stairs.

Suddenly all eyes turned back to the road, for there almost in a straight line marched a thousand burning candles and torches.

"Why, it's a torch parade!" said Pa.

Like a glowworm inching its way through the dark, the torch parade was heading toward the provincial capitol across the park, beside the hospital. Now it was right in front of the Santos Cuyugan house. The glittering torches held high by men, women, and children were evenly paced in the middle of the road. Those without torches held up placards bearing the same words that they were shouting. Others walked empty handed, rhythmically chanting: *Mabuhay! Mabuhay ang Anti! Mabuhay ang Partido Nacionalista!*

Ma and Pa reached the porch. They, too, cheered as they stood side by side, the baby between them. The children each took a peek at the baby but for the moment the parade caught all their attention. Ma went in with the baby and put her to bed.

Ceres did not understand what the parade was for, what the chanting meant. "What's this, what's this?" she asked.

"Once I heard Pa tell Ma he's an Anti," said Mario.

"What's an Anti?" asked Ceres.

"No," said Ruben. "Pa said he is Nacionalista. "

"Pa is Anti and he is Nacionalista, same," said Mario.

So Pa explained. "You remember I talked to you about Quezon? Senate President Quezon?" Pa asked the children.

The five, including Tecla, nodded, their eyes lit up by the torches passing down the road below. They had indeed heard about Quezon. Pa and Ma were always talking about him.

"He's an important man, the big one," said Ruben.

"Well," Pa continued. "The Senate President is the head of our Senate which makes laws to run our country, but these laws should adhere to the Constitution, not oppose it. But we don't have a Constitution of our own yet. So our laws should not oppose the American Constitution, that's what rules us: the American Constitution."

"Oh, so we're Americans?" asked Mario.

"No, of course not," said Pa. "Quezon is our Filipino leader, the leader of our country. But he is not yet the Chief Executive, the president. We are not yet independent. We are fighting, still fighting to be free. The American government rules us. It wants us to accept the "freedom" it offers us, in the way we do not want it. The American government, it gives what it thinks we need, not what we know we need. Is that too hard for you to understand?"

The children did not answer.

"And so we are against what the American government has offered," Pa continued. "The Hare-Hawes Cutting Law, the HHC. There are those who are for it, they are Pro. Quezon is Anti. We, we are Anti — against. *Mabuhay ang Anti!*"

"*Mabuhay ang Anti! Mabuhay ang Anti!*" Mario, Ceres, Ruben joined him. They too wanted to be free. And besides, it was fun to shout what Pa believed in even if they did not fully understand him.

The torches were now marching around the corner of one section of the park leading straight to the capitol ground. Smoke filled the cool night air. All of a sudden amidst the chanting and cheering, three shots burst out.

"Firecrackers! Like New Year!" Mario exclaimed.

"No, those are gun shots," Pa said slowly.

Ma rushed out from the bedroom. She looked frightened. "What's that? What's that?" she cried.

No one answered her. They all looked down to the street below. There was a general hush in the crowd. The torches stopped moving. The other people not carrying torches just milled around. No one seemed to know what was happening. For a long time the parade stood still. The head of the long line had reached the capitol. The tail it seemed was still far behind in the downtown area near the church. Somewhere in the glowing curved line there was a break between the park and the capitol.

All of a sudden, like a thief in the night, a man came darting up the front stairs.

"Doctor, Doctor," he panted, "come quickly! A man has been shot. He's been brought to the hospital."

"I knew it," said Pa. "I'm coming. Get into the car!"

Pa lost no time in getting to his car. He did not bother to put on his working shoes. He rushed out in his moccasin-like leather slippers.

The crowd gave way to let his Essex pass through. In the dark, it disappeared. Ma and the children watching in the porch lost sight of its silver glint among the towering torches.

In the hospital everybody was asking each other: Who was he? How was he shot? Who shot him? Why? Why?

Pa did not ask questions. Nor answer them. As soon as he got out of his car, he walked briskly to the hospital entrance. There, the people recognized him, and stood aside to let him pass. He ordered the patient brought into the operating room. He himself went straight to the locker room where he changed into the surgeon's loose gown. Ceres called this the mu-mu. It looks like a ghost, she said, because it was long, white, and flowing.

Two policemen suddenly appeared at the door of the operating room. The nurses told them they could not get in.

"But we want to see the doctor. We want to talk to him," they said.

Pa, with his gloved hands held up high, approached them.

"Get out, get out! I talk to no one," he roared.

When Pa was at work, his mind fully concentrated on what he was to do, he could not be disturbed. Not when the life or death of a person, no matter who, was in his hands. Should anyone or anything intrude into that mind, even for a moment, Pa would surely blow his top. And now he was shaking with anger. The policemen understood. They withdrew. Two nurses shut the door. In half a minute, Pa was himself again.

The patient lay on the operating table. "He was shot so close to the heart," Pa mumbled through the gauze mask strung across his nose and mouth. "The torch was not bright enough. The killer missed by a quarter of an inch. Whew!" he said out loud.

After the operation Pa was told there had been a fight. That this man was Pro, the other Anti. This man had shouted, *Mabuhay ang Pro, Mabuhay ang Philippine Independence sa HHC!* And the other had shouted back, *Mabuhay ang Anti, Anti-HHC!* We want immediate, absolute, complete independence. You can't win, Pro. And this man had answered, Oh sure, we'll win. *Mabuhay ang Pro.* And then three shots felled this man.

Pa did not linger around to hear more. The two policemen returned to ask how the patient was doing. Pa said he thought the man would pull through. It was not too bad.

The crowd everywhere had dispersed. Back home, everybody was still awake, awaiting Pa. Like the policemen, Ma and the children wanted to know whether the man who was shot would live. Pa had the same answer. "I think so. It's not too bad." Then he added, as if he was talking to himself.

"People fight and fight. For big things, for small things. For life, for death. For freedom, for slavery."

"That man, Pa," Ruben asked, "was he fighting for life? Or for death?"

Pa smiled. He put his arms around Ruben.

"Oh, you little one. Did you understand that? Well, that man, why, that man was not fighting for freedom. He was fighting for strangulation, for tyranny, for the death of freedom. He was a Pro."

"Oh Pa, don't say that," said Ma. "We are all fighting for freedom, Anti or Pro. Only our leaders are Anti or Pro. No Filipino, no one, I don't believe any one truly wants tyranny or slavery for himself and his fellow men and for his country."

Pa put his arms around Ma too.

"My dear beloved Filipina," he murmured as he kissed her.

Hallelujah

The sun was still very bright at five o'clock in the afternoon. It was still bright at six o'clock. Fides could not tell the time by the big clock in the living room. Ma taught her.

"It's about time you learned," said Ma, "because soon you will be going to school. If you can tell time, you won't be late. "

Ma rang her little *escritorio* bell at six o'clock for the Angelus prayers. No matter what the children were doing, where they were, when they heard Ma's bell they had to come around to the little altar in her room to recite the Angelus together. The children were still playing kick-the-can in the yard. The sun had barely dipped. It was still high up, hot and bright.

Ma rang her bell a second time.

"The Angel of the Lord declared unto Mary," Ma began.

"But, Ma," Mario, Ceres, and Ruben protested, panting as they rushed in.

"It's still bright outside," said Mario.

"It's not yet night," said Ceres.

"It's .... " said Ruben.

"Shhhh," Ma hushed them. She pointed to her wrist watch. Mario looked over her shoulder. She was right. It was six o'clock.

After the prayers, Ma explained why the days seemed longer and the sun brighter. "You see, the earth, our earth, goes around the sun in one year. Like this," and she put a saucer on the table and pointed her finger around and around it. "This saucer is the sun and the tip of my finger is us, the earth. When our part of the earth — where are we?"

"The Philippines!" the children chorused.

"Okay, when the Philippines is tilted toward the sun, that is during the months of April and May," she pointed to a dot on the tip of her finger facing the saucer, "more direct rays strike us, it is summer here, the days are longer than the cold nights. Well, now it is April. "

Soon it was the Holy Week. The children knew when it was the Holy Week. There were processions and processions in the church, on the street, almost every day of the week. Even in Manila it had been like that. Ma told them as she had been telling them all these years, that it was because the little Jesus was no longer a child. He had become a man. And on Good Friday He was nailed to the Cross by the "bad men." Ma showed them while they watched the procession how sad the face of the Mother Mary was, because her son Jesus had died.

"And we are all sad because of that," Ma said. "There will be no piano playing, no noise, no loud laughter. "

The children obeyed her. It seemed everybody felt the sadness of the day. Everywhere it was quiet. Tecla and Deling did not come to their house. There was no shouting to be heard in the street or from neighborhood yards. Not even whistling. The birds in the acacia trees held up their songs. The crickets too. The neighbor's dogs ran about but did not bark. The wind was still.

All morning Ma knitted sweaters and socks. Pa took out his piles of reading materials. He read a book and then he wrote on a long pad paper. Ceres played *sungka* quietly with Fides. Mario played skipping rope all by himself. Ruben arranged and stacked up his collection of books.

The next day was the *Sabado de Gloria*. Jesus would rise and live again. When Ruben asked why, if He was dead, Ma said because He was God. And because He lived again, they could all be happy. They could make all the noise and merrymaking they wanted. Everyone would rejoice and shout, "*Mabuhay si Hesus!* God is risen! Jesus lives again!"

Just before the church bells rang that morning, Tecla came and awakened the children, whispering to each of them. To Mario, she said, "When you hear the bells, that is when Jesus lives again. You must jump as high as you can, if you want to grow some more, tall and straight. "

"But I'm already tall and straight," said Mario.

To Ceres, Tecla whispered: "Let your Ma and Pa pull you up from the bottom of your neck, up, up, like this," and she lifted the chubby girl off her feet, holding her up by the neck.

"Oh, I'm too heavy now," said Ceres.

To Ruben, Tecla whispered: "Run to a high branch of a tree, any tree, that you can reach, jump to it, pulling yourself up and down, up and down. That'll let you grow up tall too. "

"Me?" Fides asked, as Tecla seemed to have forgotten her.

"Oh, don't worry, your Ma and Pa will pull you up too," Tecla assured her.

When the bells did ring, the spell of silence was instantly broken. Everyone jumped and shouted, "*Mabuhay si Hesus! Mabuhay si Hesus!*"

"Lift me, lift me high!" cried Ceres to her Ma.

"Me, too!" cried Fides.

Ma held her little girls' faces in her hands one at a time, and raised each two inches from the floor. Mario and Ruben dashed down the stairs, jumped high, gripped a branch of an acacia tree in the backyard and hung on to it, shouting as loud as they could, "Jesus, Jesus, Jesus is risen!"

And so it was Easter.

In the church patio the next day, Sunday, the risen God was going to meet His beloved Mother in a corner there, already decorated like Heaven. *Cadena de amor* vines entwined four tall bamboo posts forming a small square supporting a little platform on top. There hung a big rosebud made of crepe paper. When the petals of this rose opened as in full bloom, a tiny girl dressed like an angel appeared. Then she was lowered down by a pulley attached to her puffy dress, slowly, ever so gently, until she was about 10 feet above the ground, and dangled there precariously, awaiting the *salubong*, the meeting of the Virgin Mother Mary and her son Jesus. The crowd watched open-eyed. The little children shouted and giggled. Pa hoisted little Fides up on his shoulder so she could see better above the crowd.

The choir of angels sang,

> *Hallelujah! for the Lord our God*
> *the almighty reigns*
> *Let us rejoice and exult and give*
> *Him the glory,*
> *Hallelujah! Hallelujah!*

Below, Virgin Mother Mary and her risen son Jesus, their faces radiant with glory, walked from opposite ends of the patio to meet each other right in the middle of the appointed spot in Heaven where hung the angel of the rose. At this point when they met, the choir sang louder and the multitude joined in praise and joy.

After Mass on their way home, Pa asked Fides,

"Wouldn't you like to be that little angel-girl winging down from heaven, hah?"

"I'd like to be an angel choir singing to Jesus," said Fides.

Trip to Baguio

The children were restless. They were getting impatient. Ma said they were going to Baguio after the Holy Week. But the Holy Week had come and gone and they were not yet packing. They knew packing was the first step in any trip they took.

Pa explained that, for two months, they would be in the Pines City, as Baguio was sometimes called. He would bring the family up there in the Essex and then he had to come down again. He had work to do. When they were ready for home, Pa would drive up again to fetch them.

"Ma, when do we start packing?" asked Mario.

"You wait, just wait for the time," said Ma.

The next day it was Ceres who asked. "Now, Ma, time now?"

Ma shook her head. "No, maybe tomorrow," she said.

Then it was Ruben. "When, Ma, really, really, when, Ma?"

"Don't ask anymore. I'll say when. Soon as Pa and I are ready," said Ma.

And so the children prepared to forget the whole thing. They roamed the coconut grove with Tecla and Deling. They had learned to gather the mushrooms without disturbing the dwarf *nuno*, by saying, "Excuse me!" as Tecla had taught them. They gathered so many, sometimes Tecla let them bring some home.

At last one day at breakfast Pa said they were leaving that very afternoon.

"Yehey-y-y-y!" shouted Mario, Ceres, Ruben, and Fides.

Pa mapped out the plan of their trip. "We're going this afternoon. We'll reach Manila after sundown when it's cooler. Manila must be sizzling now. Spend the night, just one night, with the Arguelles family — you know, the godmother of Ceres. Why suffer Manila's heat! The next day we leave for Baguio. But first we'll stop over for early lunch at your Lolo and Lola's in San Fernando, Pampanga. We'll reach Baguio with my easy driving in the early evening. There, how about that?"

"Yehey-y-y-y!" was all the children could answer.

Packing was not an easy matter. It was cold in Baguio. They would have to pack not only their fine clothes but also flannels and sweaters. To the children it was like a game— which to bring, which to leave behind. Sometimes Ma objected to their choices but mostly she didn't.

At last they piled in with their baggage into the old Essex. Tecla and Deling stood at the front gate waving at them. Ma had begged Tecla to stay in the house while they were away. Tecla assured Ma she and Deling would take care of the house; they could leave their nipa hut in the woods for two months. Pa started the motor and drove on.

Manila was fully-lighted when Pa drove the Essex down the end of the north road that led to the very heart of Quiapo. Then he stopped at the corner of Calle Raon right in front of the church. Doctor and Mrs. Manuel Arguelles, and their son Loging, greeted them at the door. They had been expecting these *provincianos*, people from the province, they joked Ma and Pa.

Ma and Pa with the girls and Ruben slept in one room. Mario

and Loging in another room.

"It's so hot, I can't sleep," complained Ruben. "And it's so noisy, can you hear that streetcar outside?"

"No, I can't," said Ceres, just to contradict him. "Never mind, tomorrow, we're going to Lolo and Lola's in San Fernando. Ohhh, hot there too. Then Baguio, you'll say it's too cold."

"Shh, go to sleep, you two," said Ma.

The next day, they were in San Fernando. Pa slowed and stopped in front of the ancient house of his pa and ma, Lolo and Lola. All around it were wide-spreading, fruit-bearing trees: *santol, tamarind, manzanita.* Everything was lovely for the kids, except for the ash all around. Ash so thick on the ground. Ash covering the house and trees. Because the sugar central was nearby, Pa explained, the ashes came from the smoke stack of the mill. Pa knew this because it was the house he grew up in. As a little boy, during the milling season in April, he used to watch the ashy smoke curl up into the air from the huge chimney. "They're cooking the sugar cane," his pa, Lolo, had said.

That was why even Pa and Ma kissed Lolo's and Lola's wrinkled hands. Mario, Ruben, Ceres, and Fides followed. Lolo and Lola blessed each of them, making the sign of the cross on each forehead, as they prayed, "May God have mercy on your soul."

There were so many aunts, uncles, cousins, nieces, and nephews, in the house. Some lived there with Lolo and Lola; others came because they knew Tatang Basiong the doctor was coming. They all gathered in the living room before lunch. Lolo and Lola sat in high-backed carved armchairs, while all the aunts, uncles, nieces, nephews, and cousins, fussed over them. They saw to it that Lolo's feet rested on a footstool. If Lola perspired, a handkerchief was promptly inserted down the back of her *camisa* until that too became damp and then they changed it with another dry, clean handkerchief.

"Ruben is tall for his age, isn't he?" an uncle said.

"And look at Mario, the picture of his Ma, with all those moles on his face," said an aunt.

"Fides is growing up fat and pretty. To think she was such an ugly duckling of a baby," said a cousin.

"Look at Ceres, like our dear dead sister, Nena, ay, even down to her tapering fingertips," said an uncle.

"But her thick eyebrows are Tatang Basiong's, see?" said another cousin.

"Ay, but when she grows up and becomes a *dalaga* lady, you'll see, she'll pluck them all out and shape them into thin lines, eh?" said another aunt.

Everybody laughed. Ceres wondered what that was all about. But she dared not interrupt the old folks' conversation. It was impolite, Ma had taught her. Later, after lunch and after all the goodbyes and wishes for a safe and happy journey were said, when they were back in the Essex, Ceres asked Ma.

"When will I become a *dalaga*, Ma?"

"Not for a long time yet, dear, when you become as tall as I. "

"When I'm eighteen?"

Ma nodded.

The Essex rumbled on the dry level road. A long stretch of a drive lay before them. Everyone dozed off. Everyone except Pa. Pa must keep awake. He must keep the car on the road. Every time he came to the next province, he called out its name.

"We're past Pampanga, Tarlac now. Next Pangasinan. "

But Ma and the children were too sleepy and tired to sit up and take notice. Fides' head lay on Ma's lap. Ma's head rested backward on the rounded edge of the back seat. Ruben's and Ceres' heads kept nodding and nodding down their chests. Mario lay curled up on the front seat beside Pa.

Suddenly Pa called out, "The longest bridge in the Philippines!"

Ruben stood up. "Where, where, Pa?" he asked, rubbing his eyes. One of Ruben's favorite things was the bridge. He loved bridges. He always cried out, "Bridge! Bridge!" whenever Pa drove across one of them as if he had just discovered it. He wondered at the gleaming silver steel, so strong and heavy it could carry a "road," he said. It could look down on the river below, if there was a river. Sometimes it looked down on a wide sandbar or a trickle of water seeking its way out of the piles and piles of rocks.

The rest of the family straightened up. They looked around dreamily. Mario and Ruben saw the policemen directing traffic.

"Look, look! They have no shoes! What's this town, Ma?" Ruben asked excitedly.

"Pozorrubio," Ma answered.

"Why, can't they buy shoes?" asked Ruben.

Ma shook her head.

"But they can buy the whistle and stick and the . . ."

"Stupid! Don't you know," Mario interrupted him, "so they can run faster after the bad men. "

"Ma, listen to Mario. Always calling me stupid. That's a bad word, no?" complained Ruben.

"That's not a bad word. You're really stupid," said Mario.

"Now, now, no fighting," Ma counselled. "Or Pa will stop the car. And we won't go to Baguio anymore. "

"We're almost there," Pa announced. "Let's have something to eat before the climb. "

He stopped by the roadside. Ma took out the sandwiches and passed them around. Then she poured cold water from a jug into paper cups and again passed them around.

Pa started up the Essex once more. "Do you notice we're starting to climb?" he asked at last.

"Really, really?" Ceres asked.

"Soon it'll be zig, zag, zig, zag, up, up we go!" Pa said.

"Yehey-y-y-y!" the four children shouted.

Then everybody was silent. Pa was putting all of his mind into his driving. It was getting difficult. The road turned sharply to the left, then to the right. To the left, to the right. Little mounds became hills. Hills became mountains. What they passed through they could soon see far below them. Down below, it became deeper and deeper as they went higher and higher, hugging the mountain, and reaching the sky. Mist blocked most of the way. Pa could not see too far beyond the nose of the Essex. He leaned forward on the wheel. He was breathing hard. He did not talk. Even the children dared not talk. They helped Pa to think and concentrate. Their ears seemed plugged with cooling air. They could not hear each other if they talked.

But they could hear the Essex straining its motor with a roaring, churning huff and puff. They could hear Pa's shifting gears at every turn. For every climb. In all their trips, Mario sat beside those gears. He watched Pa's hands move them. And the Essex heaved up and forward. Forward, upward, upward.

Pine trees began to appear. First one, two, a few. Then more and more stood like marching soldiers on the slopes. At last they filled up a whole mountain. All of the mountains full of marching stately pines. There were no other trees. Just pine and grass and fern. The air began to smell of pine. Cold air that smelled of burning pine. For the children that was the beginning of Baguio. Cold pine-smelling air that opened a whole new world to them.

Summer Cousins

In Baguio, they visited with the family of Teodoro Arvisu, a good friend of Pa and Ma, and the director of the Baguio General Hospital, in a cottage sitting on the very top of a hill.

From afar the red-painted cottage looked like a red candy dropped in a forest of pine. But as their car turned a bend sloping upwards, other little candy drops appeared — blue and white dahlias, red and purple snap dragons, yellow daisies and sunflowers, red carnations, and golden everlasting flowers scattered all over the garden. The good sun poured out all its warmth and strength on these little plants, for the pine trees stood out of the way. They remained crowding each other on the slopes.

Teodoro Arvisu was a doctor like Pa, and his wife, Miguela Arvisu, was a nurse like Ma. They had four children: Teddy, Cesar, Nalie, and Lourdes, who were almost of the same ages as Mario, Ceres, Ruben, and Fides. The two families had so much in common. Living under the same roof and playing the same games, the children became inseparable. For them, for years, summer vacation meant being together, exchanging visits. They called each other's Pa and Ma, Uncle and Auntie. More than friends, they were like cousins. Summer cousins, they said. Summer was the hot season of the year in the months of April and May in the lowlands. It was also the time of vacation for schoolchildren.

Pa rested for only a day after they arrived in Baguio before he started back to Lucena, back to the grind as he said.

One day, Ma and Auntie went to the city market and Uncle, to work in the hospital. Two maids in the Arvisu household, whose names were Vising and Atring, looked after the children and cleaned the house. The children planned their own activities.

"What'll we do today?" asked Ceres.

"I know," said Teddy. "Let's explore."

"What's explore?" asked Fides.

"Stupid! That means to look around," said Mario.

"For what?" asked Nalie.

"Anything," said Mario.

"For caves," said Teddy.

"Yes, yes, let's look for caves!" they all shouted. They rushed out into the sunshine.

"Where do we start?" asked Cesar.

"At the back of the house. We'll start sliding down there," said Teddy. He was the leader of the day. Whoever thought of the idea gave the orders. That was their rule.

They rushed back in to get their "sleds." These were carton boxes with the top flaps open. Each owned one to ride in. It just glided down the slippery pine needle-covered slope. Sometimes it bumped into a tree. Carton box, foolish head, and all. But it did not hurt much. It was fun, everyone agreed.

Vising saw them stealing away with their "sleds."

"Hoy, hoy, hoy, where you going, hah? You can't go. No permission from your mamas, they're not here."

"Just sliding down, please, please, just sliding," pleaded Teddy.

"All right, all right, but no foolishness, hah! Or I'll tell you to your mama. And don't go too far away. And take care of the two small ones!"

They all rushed out again. The sun was already high, frowning down upon them. Teddy chose the slope that curved directly down to a narrow flat treeless ground. The Baguio General Hospital sat on this little flat land.

"But Uncle said we must not go there. There are so many germs there," said Ruben.

"We'll just land there first. Then there's another slope somewhere. We go down from there," directed Teddy.

All agreed. Everyone sat inside his or her sled. One, two, ready, go! Where the pine needles were thick on the ground, the sled went fastest. At the first landing, they met again. They were careful no one from the hospital saw them, most of all, Uncle. He would surely bring them back home in his car. Then, Teddy led the way to another slope.

"Here, follow me," he said. He got on his sled and started down. Down, down, down he went. The others followed him. Down, down, down they went.

Suddenly Fides' sled went straight for a tree. She could not stop. She could see the tree coming right smack into her face. She closed her eyes. Bump! There she was holding onto the small trunk of the tree. Her sled had gone right on sliding down, down, down, without her. She began to cry. She kept wiping the blood from a little cut on her upper lip. That didn't hurt. That was not what she was crying about.

"I want a box. My box is gone. I want a box," she cried.

Ruben heard her. He rushed to her side and said, "You want a box? You want a box? Here!" and he boxed her.

Fides cried louder and louder. The others gathered around her. Ruben had to explain.

"She said she wanted a box. So I gave her one."

Everyone laughed. Fides cried louder. Ceres remembered that Dar had played the same joke on her a long time ago.

"That's an old trick," she told Ruben. "You are really like Dar, Ma said."

Then Teddy said, "Okay, okay. Let's put away our sleds. Let's begin walking."

They piled their sleds to one side of a tree, covered them with dry needles and brushwood. Then they began walking. The grass and ferns were thicker and taller down there. There was still no sight of a cave. They walked and walked. It was hot. They started to perspire. The sun looked like a huge golden melting pancake stuck to the pointed tops of the pine trees. They were going down into the ravine.

Fides had stopped crying. Now she was complaining. "I'm thirsty. I want a drink."

"Me too," said Lourdes.

"Ssssst, stop! Look!" exclaimed Mario.

Covered with vines and ferns and grasses, the dark cavity could hardly be seen. It was a little hole in the mountain. Mario pushed the clinging vines aside and peeped in. "It's so dark I can't see," he said.

"Let me, let me see. Yes, yes, it's a cave. It's a cave!" cried Teddy. "We've found a cave!"

Mario and Teddy started to clear the way into the cave. Ruben, Cesar, Ceres, Nalie, Lourdes, and Fides hurried down. All together with their bare hands they ripped out the fern leaves and tall cogon grasses. Mario peeped in once more. He stepped forward. Teddy followed. All the rest followed. They stood upright inside. Everyone stood still. Where the light could not get in it was dark. Teddy stretched out his arm upward. He touched ferns and earth.

"Oh, it's just a small cave," he sighed. "Come on, let's look for another one."

Just then outside the sky darkened. Raindrops fell. Thunder

echoed back and forth. They stepped back into the cave. Teddy decided they should take shelter there should the rains pour. Fides started to cry again.

The rains poured down rapidly. Mist gathered like puffs of smoke blown into their faces. They could not see one inch away from each other. Huddled close together, afraid to move and lose one another, they looked like a big stump of a tree at the mouth of the cave. They could not hear anything beyond the howling of the wind and the rain and the hissing swish of the pine tree tops.

Even Fides' shrill piercing cry was like the echo of the wind and the rain. And lost in the cry and echo of the wind and the rain, somewhere, was Uncle's call. "T-e-d-d-y! C-e-s-a-r!" He called everyone of them. "Mario! Ruben!" But his voice melted in the mist. "Nalie! Ceres! F-i-d-e-s! L-o-u-r-d-e-s!"

Mario thought he heard someone calling them. Then he saw a spot of light in the slope. At first he thought it was the sun. It kept flickering and flickering. It kept moving and moving. It was coming nearer and nearer.

"It's Uncle!" exclaimed Mario at last.

Uncle was so happy he had found them. With him were Vising and Atring who helped gather them all up. Vising had umbrellas to hold over Fides and Lourdes. Atring had raincoats to wrap around the rest of them. It was difficult to climb the slippery slope. Most of the way Uncle pushed them up on their buttocks. Or he pulled them up by the hands. Then before they reached the house, he lifted Fides and Lourdes, one in each arm and carried them across the sloshy backyard right through the kitchen door. Ma and Auntie were waiting for them in the kitchen. Without saying a word, no explanations, no scoldings, they got the children to bed, after a quick warm water scrub and bath and cups of hot chicken broth. Time enough to hear their story in the morning.

Outside, the rains beat down harder and harder, like a thousand hooves of horses, upon the roof. The thunder roared like a pack of wild tigers and lions smashing down the hills, echoing from hill to hill. The children, now cozily tucked into their beds felt how good it was to be warm and dry and safe under the folds of thick flannel blankets. Let it rain outside. Let the rain pour over the trees, the grass, the stones, all over the earth. Let the thunder and lightning smash the mountains to pieces. As long as they had their pa and ma, brothers and sisters, summer cousins, and the warm blankets, nothing else mattered.

"What happened to our sleds? Think they're all soaking wet?" asked Ceres.

"Of course, stupid!" said Mario.

"We can get new ones from the grocery, don't worry," said Teddy. Then he whispered under the blanket. "We'll call our cave, Tiny Cavy. "

Ghost! Ghost!

One night, Ma, Uncle, and Auntie were dressing up for an evening out. Ma and Auntie were putting on glittering gowns called *saya*. Fides watched them slip into the big puffed-up sleeves. She wondered when she too would be allowed to wear such a beautiful dress. But she did not ask Ma. She did not ask Ma either where she and Auntie and Uncle were going. She knew they were going to a party of "very important people" as Ma had always said, on such occasions.

Ma pinned down the upper portion of the *saya* to the long flowing skirt, at the waistline. Without being told, Fides handed her the pins from the pin cushion. Then Ma brushed up her long black hair and piled all of it into a top-knot at the back of her head. In her high-heeled shoes she walked slowly from end to end of the room, once in a while looking at herself in the mirror. Part of the long skirt trailed after her like a tail. She bent backwards a little, picked it up, and carried it folded and hanging over her arm. Fides giggled. She thought it was a funny way to carry a tail.

Ma and Auntie took a long time to dress. Uncle was already waiting out in the living room in his thick dark suit, smoking a cigar.

When they finally left, Mario and Teddy heaved a sigh of relief. "Aha, now we can play Ghost! Ghost!" they shouted.

Teddy ran to the corner main electric box to switch off all the lights. The house plunged into complete darkness. Except for the uncertain moonlight shivering outside among the pine trees that drifted in through the glass windows, there was no light. The children could not see each other as long as no one drifted into the path of the moonlight.

Vising and Atring played with the children. Vising was the first Ghost. Draping a white bedsheet around her body like a white ghost, she counted from one to one hundred. Everybody scampered away. Ceres and Nalie held each other and promised to hide together. Some of the boys went under the beds, the rest into closets full of thick coats and dresses. Atring stood behind the thick curtains in the living room. Then Vising the Ghost went around looking for them. The first one she caught was Cesar whose foot was sticking out of a bed. After the others had been found, Cesar was the Ghost.

This time no one was allowed to pair with another. "Each to your own hiding place, hah?" warned Cesar.

Fides jumped into a bed and covered herself with all the blankets and pillows she could gather fast. Lourdes followed, but in another bed, just beside Fides. But Fides did not know that. She was too far inside her little cave of blankets.

It seemed such a long time for Cesar to come, thought Fides. She peeped out for a moment. She heard a faint rattling of a kettle, it seemed. Vising and Atring probably were in the kitchen, she thought. Then the rattling stopped. All quiet. Dark.

Fides slid back underneath the mountain of blankets and pillows. She wondered. Where was everybody? Where was Cesar the Ghost? Why didn't he come out yet? While she was waiting and waiting, not daring to breathe with a sound, she began to feel something move. It was the pillow perched on top of her head. It was being lifted up. Fides opened her eyes. But there was a thin sheet covering her face. Soon that too was being lifted up. Fides dared not move. She closed her eyes. Suddenly a cold, dry — no, it was dripping wet — thing touched her cheeks. She jumped and shrieked, "Ghost! Ghost!" And she began to cry.

Just then the blinking lights of Uncle's car shone round the bend. Vising and Atring called all of them to come out.

"They're back! They're back! Come out now, all of you!"

All dashed out of their hiding places, like little mice scurrying out of their holes. Teddy quickly switched on the lights. Fides saw the frozen pieces of chicken dripping like melting ice cubes which Cesar had held over her cheeks, and was now sprinkling on everyone's faces, laughing all the while and mimicking Fides as she shrieked, Ghost! Ghost! Everyone helped put everything back in order: the cushions in the sofas and chairs in the living room, the blankets and pillows in the beds. Then Vising gathered them around the fireplace. "I'll tell you a story," she said.

Thus, all the good little children were gathered quietly around the fire listening to Vising when Uncle, Auntie, and Ma came in through the front door.

"My, my, that's a long, long story," said Ma. "Isn't it bedtime?"

"One more short one, Ma. Vising has just begun," pleaded Ruben.

Ma nodded. Vising began her story:

> Kabunian is the name of the god of the mountain
> province. He used to come to earth which he had
> created. Every time he saw it he felt unhappy,
> because there were no people in it. And because
> there were no people, there was no laughter.
> One day, Kabunian decided to do something
> about it. He took some clay and molded the images
> of two people out of it — one of a man, and
> another of a woman.

And so Kabunian said to himself: I'll make them laugh.
Then they'll be alive.
So saying, he caught a chicken and plucked
off all its feathers. Then he poked it with his
finger, so that it jumped.
At this, one of the images came to life and
laughed — becoming the first man. The other image
heard the first one laugh, laughed also, and
became the first woman.

Only Ceres and Ruben were still awake, rubbing the sand dust in their eyes.

"One more, please?" Ceres begged sleepily.

"One more?" asked Ruben.

"Sh-h-h-h!" whispered Vising.

The President's Telegram

*I*t was a foggy day. Pa arrived the day before to bring the family back to the lowlands. Back to Lucena. It was the end of summer. Time to say goodbye to the Arvisus and the mountains till next summer.

"Take care of Tiny Cavy," Mario shouted.

"And the ghost," Ruben shouted.

"And Kabunian," Ceres shouted.

"And the chicken," Fides shouted.

Ma and Pa were puzzled. What were the children saying? But their thoughts were now occupied with the trip back home. Pa nodded and waved his hand to the Arvisus standing by the front door, before he turned to the wheel.

The sun had not touched the chilly earth. Clouds hung about like curtains. The pebbled road that wound down the steep hill was still moist with the early morning dew. Clouds instead of dust followed the trail of their car. But ahead the sun was now clearing the way. And soon they were zigzagging down the wide open highway, leaving behind for another year, the clouds and the cold and the pine trees.

And their summer cousins.

Ceres wished they didn't have to leave. She wished they could have lived there forever. But then she thought of home and Deling and Tecla and their little nipa hut in the woods, and the aratiles trees in the hospital yard, and school, oh yes, school was all right now, and she was glad they were going back home. She had realized from the incessant talk of Pa and Ma and from what she had seen they did to help the sick, the dying, and the poor, that as long as she shared what she had, it was all right. It was all right to be different, to be rich. It was all right to be happy with what Pa and Ma had for her. It was so good to have all these — a nice home, summer vacations with summer cousins, Christmas pageant and gift-sharing with so many poor children. All because of Pa and Ma. From the back of the car, she hugged Pa tight.

"Hey, hey, what's all this about?" Pa grinned.

Ceres hugged him again. Pa liked that.

Suddenly there was a man on the road with a red banner. He was flagging them down. Pa stopped the car. The man walked directly to Pa's side and asked him "Doctor Santos Cuyugan?"

"Yes," answered Pa.

"A telegram from the President," was the man's reply as he handed over to Pa a small sheet of bluish paper.

Pa read it fast. Without saying a word, he started up the car and drove down the winding road as fast as he could. It was as if the Essex was flying, its wheels barely touching the ground.

"Pa, you're getting reckless," warned Ma, as she held on to the back of the front seat.

"The President. He wants me to be at the pier at one o'clock. Wants me to accompany him to Iloilo, just in case," Pa answered breathlessly.

Ceres knew what Pa meant. The President was President Manuel Quezon. He was no longer the Senate President. Pa had explained that he had been elected President of the Commonwealth of the Philippines. She often heard Pa and Ma talk about him. He was Pa's patient, and at one time he had dysentery and developed appendicitis. He began to pass bloody stools which Pa said were a saving means of nature because one artery in the appendix raptured but the bleeding was taking place inside the colon not outside. So the decision was not to operate. Don Tomas Earnshaw, mayor of Manila, had a similar case, Pa said, and the Mayor's wife wanted Pa to take charge of the ailment when half a dozen surgeons could not agree whether to operate or not.

Another of Pa's favorite stories about the President was when he and the President once travelled down south and they lay side by side in a ship's cabin, each of them reading a book. They had agreed that whoever turned in last at night, would turn off the light. "He's such a voracious reader, the President," Pa had said. "He was always the last to turn in." Another time, Ceres actually saw the President when he visited at their house in Lucena. He sat on one of their rattan chairs. He stood up and sat on another. Then he returned to the first one. Ma called out to Ceres and her brothers and sister who were peeping from the bedroom, to play the piano or sing to the visitor. But they ran away to hide. They would rather not see the President, if they had to perform for him too. And so they didn't get to see much of him.

Now Pa was speeding down the road through towns and fields and vales. He did not stop at the ancient house of Lolo and Lola in San Fernando as was his yearly route. He did not stop anywhere for lunch. He drove straight to Manila, to the pier at the North Harbor.

A big inter-island ship was waiting for the President. And Pa. So many people milled around waiting too. Pa drove through the crowd inch by inch until he could park alongside the big ship. Pa got off. He walked toward the ship and was met by a man. They talked for a while before Pa led the man to his car.

"Ma, he'll drive you over to Lucena. 'Bye now, I'll be back in a week or two," Pa said. "Oh, by the way, pack me a few clothes, Ma."

Before he could finish, Ma had already pulled out his small bag of clothes and toothbrush, which he had packed in Lucena, and handed it over to him. Then he buzzed Ma and the children on their cheeks before he turned away.

The air was sizzling hot and dusty. The crowd had thickend. Not a sniff of the fresh air from the sea broke through. Ma was fanning herself furiously only to whip up more hot air, when she remembered they hadn't had lunch. So she brought out the sandwiches and water jug, to the great relief of everybody.

The man who was to drive their car started the motor and drove away. In three hours they were home. It had been a long day. Ceres, Fides, Mario, and Ruben could hardly wait to spill their stories to Tecla and Deling about the mountains and Tiny Cavy and Kabunian, and their summer cousins.

Growing

*T*he Santos Cuyugan family was growing and growing fast. It was not only Pa's and Ma's children who were growing, their household too was expanding with many relatives coming to live with them. Soon Tecla could not keep track of the people in the house.

"It's like the mushroom in the bamboo stumps. Once you have a spore, there's no end to the multiplying. Unless you picked them all out. But you can't do that," she said. "Yes," she kept babbling, "the Santos Cuyugan family is like a mushroom spore, there is no end to its multiplying and growing. May God have mercy on your family." Then she started singing, "*Singkuling my little girl. . .* "

Fides was now a schoolgirl. She has been a very tiny baby on that stormy night she came into this world. Ma had said then she could not believe she was her child at all; she had looked like a little black mouse. "Hush, Ma 'am. Do not say so. You'll see, she'll be your pride and joy one day," Tecla had said then, babbling as always. Ma had merely smiled at that. Now, Fides was fat and pretty. Her eyes large and shiny black. Most unique of all, she had such a lovely singing voice. When she went to school at the Magills' Kindergarten, she was the envy of all the singing canaries, who feared the competition.

Ruben was in the elementary school. He loved reading books. Ma and Pa could not keep up with his reading. There were no more books in town to buy nor in the library or school to borrow. On Ma's pre-Christmas shopping trips to Manila, she never failed to include among her toy purchases, books, stacks of books for Ruben. As soon as he got them, he would sit in the big sofa in the corner of the living room, and nobody and nothing could disturb him from his books. Ruben would be so engrossed in his reading, that Ma said you could put a bomb under his seat, blow him to smithereens, and he'd still be holding fast to his book. He had read all twenty volumes of *Journeys Through Bookland* that Ma got him last Christmas. He was now reading volumes of the *Book of Knowledge* and *Mark Twain's Huckleberry Finn* and *Tom Sawyer.*

Mario was in high school. He had learned to swim and he and a bunch of his classmates loved to go swimming in the deep Iyam river not far away from school. They would cut classes just to take a quick dip. But one day their teacher got wind of their escapade, and reported the matter to the principal who called their parents. That was the end of school in Lucena for Mario. For the next school year, Pa and Ma decided to send him to Manila to board with the Arguelles family and go to school at the De La Salle College with the Arguelles's son Loging. The Arguelleses were strict disciplinarians and Pa believed they could control Mario and he would be in good company with Loging. Mario liked this arrangement. It would be a new adventure for him to study in the big city and live with Loging.

As for Ceres, she was doing quite well in school, in spite of her initial feeling of inferiority and isolation for being more privileged than her schoolmates. She had gotten over that. She was promoted to Grade V from Grade IV in the middle of the school year— it was called "acceleration," which meant she was doing advanced work way ahead of her classmates. The next year she was in Grade VI, and once more she was accelerated to Grade VII in the middle of the academic year. As class and later school declaimer, she won praises and prizes for her dramatic declamations. In the inter-provincial contest held at a big hall in town, she represented her school and town. It was a big affair, with the whole town and guests from other towns and provinces, and of course Pa and Ma and the family, in attendance. Her piece was entitled, "Nobody's Child." She was dressed in rags, barefooted, and her teacher dabbed patches of charcoal and ash over her face and legs. She was not nervous at all. In fact, she thought nothing of it, for in her heart she was acting out a child, the poorest of the poor that she had always been in company with at play, in school, and in her make-believe world. She did so well, reciting her very sad piece, that all the mothers and fathers in the audience were wiping tears in their eyes when she finished and bowed to their thunderous applause. So convincing was she as "nobody's child."

Pa and Ma hugged her tight after the program when it was announced that she won the first prize.

"But you are our child — not nobody's," they said proudly. Everybody was congratulating Pa and Ma as if they, too, had won.

Ma's second cousin, Emilia Belza, and her two nieces, Cilia and Tem Belza, both orphans, came to live with the Santos Cuyugan family. Ma taught Emilia to sew. There were lots of things to sew. The boys and girls were fast outgrowing their clothes— shirts and trousers, chemises, and dresses. They needed new ones. Emilia learned to use Ma's old Singer Sewing machine. Ma also taught her to embroider. As a schoolgirl, Ma was a *colegiala* in a convent school where she had learned expert embroidery. In those days, she said, no girl grew up to become a lady and get married without having mastered the art of sewing and embroidery; the more intricate the designs and stitches she made, the more popular she would be.

Ma sent Cilia, who was ten years old, to school. Tem was seven but stood just over two feet tall. Ma said she had to grow up some more before she'd go to school.

"I have a cousin, a real first cousin," Fides boasted to Deling. "She's the same age as me, but small. Name's Tem. "

Tem began to cry. She heard her name and knew Fides was talking about her.

"She's crying because she has no mama," said Fides.

"None?" asked Deling.

"None," said Fides.

"What about your mama?" asked Deling.

"My mama is my mama, not hers," said Fides. "I'll ask Ma." Then she called out Ma. "Ma, are you also the ma of Tem?"

"Why no, child," said Ma. "Her pa and ma were my brother and sister, they're dead now. That's why she's come to live with us. I'm her auntie. I guess that's like being her ma. She can call me Ma too. "

"I'll tell her so she'll stop crying," said Fides.

More cousins and nieces of Pa and Ma came to live with them. From Ma's side from Buhi and Pa's side from San Fernando. There were the sisters Choling and Dulce Noble, and Paquita Belza, all second cousins of Ma. At first, they were only visiting. Then, Pa offered Choling work as hospital attendant. Choling was too surprised and shy to accept at first.

"Yes, yes, Pa," Ceres answered for her. "Tia Choling will work here and stay with us. "

Dulce and Paquita became Ma's tennis and pingpong partners. Pa and Ma had taken to tennis and pingpong playing as their exercise. The cousins were a great help, too, when Ma entertained friends at home. They baked cakes and pastries, with Ceres and Fides helping a bit. Ma did not want her two daughters working too often in the kitchen since they started taking piano lessons. "Your hands will become too rough and stiff from too much soap and water washing," she said to the girls. And so the girls kept away from too much manual work in the kitchen, at the laundry, or in the garden. Even Ruben, who had begun piano and violin lessons, was told to keep his hands supple and soft. "Your hands and heart for music," Ma had said. It was one of her aspirations for her children to be great musicians someday.

When Pa's nieces from San Fernando came to visit, there was no question they too would be asked to stay. They were Maria and Adela Santos. Both had graduated from teaching courses in Manila, with book allowance from Pa. Maria accepted a teaching position at the Tayabas Provincial High School; Adela, at the Lucena Elementary School. Ma would not let the two sisters live all by themselves. "There will be room for you here, always room for one more." Ma's words were final.

Then there was Luis Carrascoso, a Spanish mestizo relative of Ma from Buhi. He affected effeminate tastes and ways and loved to put on a lady's skirt and blouse, then wrap a flower-printed bed coverlet around his whole body. He struck a very noble attitude, with arms stretched upward and his head tilted back, as he announced in a stentorian voice, "Who wants to go to hell with Madam Satan?"

"Me, me, me!" the children cried, one by one.

One day, Pa put him to work at the hospital, as an attendant like Choling. That morning Luis went swishing down the stairs and Ceres who was often up early with the sun, saw him and called out, "Where you going, Madam Satan?"

"Why, to hell!" he shouted back.

"Me too, me too!" cried Ceres.

But he was off before Ceres could catch up with him.

There was Pa's youngest brother Juan whom the children fondly called Uncle John. He had just arrived from the United States where he graduated as a doctor from the University of Illinois. Uncle John said he had seen Pa's life-like anatomy drawings exhibited there, many years after Pa had left the school. Now Uncle John returned to the Philippines to practice in his home country, just like Pa. He was invited by Pa to be a resident-physician at the hospital.

Uncle John was such a handsome dashing young eligible bachelor, there was not a lady in town who, at one time or another, did not try to bait him, so enamored of him were they. But he did not take anyone seriously. In the end the ladies, in desperation, resorted to all sorts of deadly tricks to avenge their unrequited love. One sent a poisoned cake to the house. Tecla, with her vaunted sixth sense, got suspicious and threw it into a garbage can out in the yard. A stray cat ate a bit of it and promptly convulsed and died. Another sent a bomb in an artfully wrapped innocent-looking box. Forewarned by Tecla, Ma sent it immediately to the police. This was the last straw. Pa finally advised his Don Juan Lothario of a brother to seek residency elsewhere, far away, in a hospital in the southern island of Mindanao.

As for Deling, Ma had finally convinced Tecla to send her daughter to school. Ceres had invited her friend to live in their house while she taught her to read and write the letters and some words and numbers. Then it had been easy for Deling to be in Grade I, skipping kindergarten. Rather late, but Ma said, "Better late than never, and remain unschooled all her life."

"Yes," acquiesced Tecla, "I didn't believe in school, in English, in America. We are so poor. We have nothing. I thought it was a joke to aspire—to change your life." Then she added, "But I seen you, Ma'am, and the Doctor."

"Oh yes, Inay," said Deling who was very shy and spoke sparingly. "Ceres teaches me. And I learn a lot in school."

"Ay, with God's help," sighed Tecla. And she sang: "*Singkuling my little girl . . .*"

When the Santos Cuyugans now prayed together at Angelus, Ma added many new names to her collection of people.

"Bless us all, ever and ever, God, don't forget," Ceres murmured softly.

Back to Manila

*T*alk of war was everywhere. It was now the most important topic discussed by the Santos Cuyugan family at the table. They kept abreast of all the events in and out of the country. The news from Europe was dark, but Europe was too far away from the United States and the Philippines. Adolf Hitler had made himself dictator of Germany and his military forces, the strongest in Europe. He became obsessed in making the Aryan German race superior over all in the world. *Deutschland Uber Alles!* He believed the Jews were not fit to live on the earth and so he devised The Final Solution — their extermination. While his Nazis, as members of his National Socialist Party were called, and his Wehrmacht — army, navy, and air forces— were rampaging all over Europe, France, Great Britain, and the Scandinavian neutrals did nothing until they found themselves faced at last with war. When Hitler attacked Poland using tanks and planes in blitzkrieg tactics, Great Britain and France declared war on Germany. Australia and New Zealand joined them. Then Canada. The United States proclaimed its neutrality as official national policy, although President Roosevelt said that he could not ask every American to remain neutral in thought as well.

In Asia, Japan had invaded China, set up a new puppet Chinese regime at Nanking, and was threatening to send troops to Indo-China. Now this concerned the United States and President Roosevelt warned Tokyo not to use the European war as a cover for aggression. Tokyo ignored this warning and instead signed with Germany and Italy a Tripartite Pact pledging joint action if any member went to war with the United States. Germany and Italy had acknowledged the leadership of Japan in Asia. The United States was slowly and inexorably being drawn into World War II.

Filipino leaders began to think of national security too. In Washington, President Quezon had approached General Douglas MacArthur and asked him to come to the Philippines to develop a military plan to make the Philippines secure even after the umbrella of American protection was removed after the Commonwealth government, and independence was fully granted. President Roosevelt appointed MacArthur as military adviser to the Commonwealth government. The Philippines now had its own Constitution but it included provisions and reservations of powers and privileges for the United States, and the Constitution had to be approved by the American President before submission to the Filipino people. The United States maintained considerable control over the Philippines.

"But Pa, I thought President Quezon is our leader, our president. Is he not Filipino? Why do we need the U. S. and to go to war?" asked Ceres at suppertime when Pa talked at length about the latest news reaching town from Manila.

"It's a long story. But I'll tell you for the hundredth time. To begin with, we are not truly independent, free. Remember the torch parade many years ago? Well, we the Anti, finally won. We made our own Constitution, our own Law, elected our own president, but we are still under the American government in many ways until after the Commonwealth in 1946, many years from now. We are not totally free. And before that, before the U. S. came over many many years ago, our people had won the revolution against Spain. But Spain sold us to the United States for $20 million!"

"Wow! Lots of money! Spain did not own us, why did it sell us? " asked Ruben.

"Because at that time Spain was at war with the United States, and when they fought here in the Philippines, Spain negotiated secretly with the United States — we surrender the Philippines to you, it said, but you pay us $20 million!" explained Pa.

"Hah! Cheater!" said Ceres.

"Yes, that's how more or less, we came to be under the United States. Of course many of our Filipino people fought back — we wanted to free, without foreigners controlling us. But in the end, the Americans said, ok, ok, stop fighting us, we will give you back your freedom. Someday," said Pa.

"When?" asked Ceres.

"Yes, that's it, when? When you are ready to rule yourselves, said the Americans. You are not capable of self-government. You are a barbarous race, dishonest, corrupt. We taught the native Indians back home to be civilized. God has been preparing all English-speaking Teutonic people for a thousand years to be superior to all, so God made us the master organizers of the world so that we can subdue and govern savage, and senile people of the world. We will teach you, they said," Pa continued.

"They said that?" asked Ceres, bewildered.

"Yes, well, yes, some of their powerful leaders said that. But not all of them. Some were totally horrified at what they were doing to us, the Filipinos. This is what one of them said, I read this: 'We are cold-bloodedly, wantonly, and abominably destroying the soul of a people who never did us an atom of harm in their lives.' " Pa paused. "It was like the voice of the anti-slavery Americans, way way back in their history. Like Abraham Lincoln. But their voices, these good Americans, they lost out to the more powerful leaders. And so they stayed on and on in our country. They ruled us, sometimes savagely, other times benevolently. They put up garrisons throughout the country. They put up schools and churches and hospitals. They put up very big businesses."

"How do you know all that, Pa?" asked Ruben.

"Well, I was there. I studied there," said Pa. Then he winked his eyes. "Anatomy wasn't all I learned there. I'd go to the libraries to read—such libraries! They really wanted me to read! But they thought I went there only to learn how to cut up people and excise the diseased organs and patch up torn ligaments and tissues of the body. But I read and read. Hey, you know I found out that the first Filipinos arrived in America in 1587, October 18 to be exact. They were called 'Luzonians' because they came from Luzon here -"

"Really? In 1587—that's how many, four hundred years ago? So they were like natives there? No, the first immigrants there?" asked Ruben.

"The first immigrant there, the first people in America came from Asia, you know. I researched that too. Thousands of years ago, the first native Americans came from Asia, so they were Asians before they were Americans, ha, ha, ha!" Pa laughed. "And the first ship built in California was by a Filipino Kapampangan— see?" Then with a serious mien, he continued. "But I also went there to learn the principles and values which are the hallmark of American society — love of liberty, the spirit which prizes liberty as the heritage of all men in all lands. Lincoln said: 'Those who deny freedom to others deserve it not for themselves.' "

"I like Lincoln," said Ruben.

"But I must tell you this," said Pa. "Lincoln freed the slaves but he also wanted to send the freed slaves back to Africa. Not only he but some other good Americans.

"The bad Americans," Pa continued, "they are disloyal to and betray the America they pledged allegiance to. I just hope we ourselves, the Filipinos, will never surrender our sovereignty. We should be like our heroes — Bonifacio, Rizal, Mabini, Malvar. I hope Quezon's loyalty will be to the Filipino people," said Pa with a sad tone in his voice.

"You Fides, what have you to say?" asked Pa.

Fides was silent, absorbing all of Pa's lecture.

So Pa continued, "Well, first of all, how did I get there to America? I've told you also a hundred times, I passed a test the American government gave and I was sent to school there. I had not finished any formal schooling here, there was the revolution against Spain and our war against America — how could I go to school? Good thing I passed the test and was chosen to study in the States. I became a doctor and returned here. That's not bad, eh? So I could teach our people hygiene and sanitation, put flush toilets in their homes, take care of the sick, the diseased lepers in Culion where I first worked, and operate on Quezon's appendix . . . and talk to you like this. Because I believe in the possibility of change. You and your children, and generations to come, you will change the world for a better one, eh?"

"My, my, Pa," interrupted Ma. "Enough of history and self - history. Back to the headlines in Manila. What else is news?"

"Now that Japan has joined the Axis — that is, Hitler's Germany and Mussolini's Italy — surely the United States will not keep away any longer. And we will be involved," warned Pa.

"We?" asked Ruben.

"Yes, we, our country will be attacked too because, look, there are U.S. military garrisons here, U.S. warships and planes and soldiers . . . "

"But not us. We don't have ships and planes and . . . " said Ceres.

"Too bad," Pa quickly interrupted Ceres. "But we're here. We have to defend our country from any invader," said Pa.

"Well, are we for Japan or for America?" asked Ceres.

"We should be loyal to America," said Pa, "because America will give us our independence, America taught us . . . "

84

This time it was Ruben who interrupted Pa. "But you said we were already free from Spain when America took over, we were already free . . . "

"Yes, but we were conquered again," said Pa. "We fought American power but we lost. How could we win against guns and bullets, we only had bolos. And our leaders, to keep their seats, their jobs, sided with the conquerors. But it is because of our relentless struggle to be free, and of America's noblest ideals, the spirit of 1776, the voice that lost out years ago, that America promises and promises to give us our freedom. And we know she will, by God she has to, or we will continue to fight for it . . . "

"Yes, yes, yes!" shouted Ceres and Ruben.

"But Japan, what do we know of Japan, what do we know of Japan, suppose she conquers us . . . ?" asked Pa.

"Japan has many toys," said Fides. "They are rich. "

"If the United States gives us independence, she does not have to fight Japan here," said Ruben, still not quite understanding what Pa had explained.

"No, but the United States is still here. That's the trouble. We don't want any other invader, of any kind or color in our land. So let's just say, we're not for any of them," said Pa.

"So if war comes, what shall we do?" asked Ruben.

"Fight!" said Ceres.

"Whom?" asked Ruben.

"Quezon says we will fight with America. Quezon is our president, we have to obey him," said Pa.

"Well, let's pray that war doesn't come to us," said Ma finally. "So what else, Pa, what else is news? Stop talking about war."

"Yes, there's another news. Brace yourselves for this," Pa announced. Everyone was all ears. "I've been asked to return to Manila."

"What!" exclaimed Ma.

"Yes, the hospital here is in good hands with the staff I've trained.

I have to go back to the PGH and the UP College of Medicine, to join the faculty again," said Pa.

This news dropped like a bombshell on Ma. The prospect of moving again, packing the children, clothes and all, and finding a new house, was too much for her. Of all the family, she was the one who had become very deeply rooted in Lucena. She had made so many friends: patients of Pa, parents of the children they invited for their Christmas pageant and gift-giving, parents and teachers of the children's schools, neighbors, church members, hospital staff, market vendors, store owners, town officials, the whole town! It would be heartbreaking to say goodbye to all of them.

"What about our school?" Ceres asked.

"No problem," said Pa who seemed to have everything all figured out. "We will go after school ends in March. Then you can enroll in new schools in Manila. The girls at the Philippine Women's College, Ruben at the Ateneo de Manila, and Mario will remain where he is now, at De La Salle. "

"What about the rest of the family and the household?" asked Ma. The house had become a *refugio* (refuge), as Ma had called it, of all the cousins, nieces, uncles, and aunties who were seeking new pastures or who had become orphans or homeless.

"Those who want to come with us are welcome," said Pa.

"Yes," seconded Ma. "Always room for one more is our eternal motto. We'll get a bigger house in Manila." Ma was resigned to the decision.

And so it was that the whole family went into high gear to map out plans to move again, this time back to Manila but to a bigger new home.

Ma in Filipina dress called Terno with the long "tail", as Senorita Bicolandia,
from Buhi, Camarines Sur

The Gervasio Santos Cuyugan family in Baguio, summer capital of the Philippines, from left to right: Ruben, Ma, Fides, Pa, Ceres and Mario standing in the back.

The Tabayas Provincial Hospital (in Lucena) doctors, nurses and staff with Director Dr. Santos Cuyugan in the middle, sitting front

Part III
1940 — 1950

We live in the present,
We dream of the future,
but we learn eternal truths from the past.

Dreams

When the Santos Cuyugans returned to Manila, they first rented a house on Remedios street. It was near the Philippine General Hospital where Pa resumed his work in the Department of Surgery, and near the schools where the children enrolled—the Philippine Women's College which had become a university, the Ateneo de Manila, and De La Salle College.

Of all the aunts, cousins, nieces, and other relatives, only Tem had come along with them. She enrolled at the PWU with Ceres and Fides. Choling married an attendant at the hospital and raised a family in Lucena. Ma lost track of Dulce who went to Baguio, and Paquita, Emilia, Cilia, and Luis, who all returned to Buhi. Maria and Adela stayed on teaching in Lucena. Uncle John got a residency at the Japanese Mintal Hospital in Davao in Mindanao, just as Pa had advised him, and later became its director. While there he married a Spanish mestiza from Zamboanga, Pilar Portas. Tecla and Deling stayed in Lucena in their little hut in the woods. Ma had introduced and recommended Tecla to the Magills who employed her permanently as their household maid to assist Pedro, and offered to help her daughter Deling through school.

A year later, the Santos Cuyugans bought a rambling bungalow on a wide lawn dotted with mango trees in Pasay, at the outskirts of Manila. They had also added a new member to the family — Ciano, a driver. Pa said he could no longer drive the kids to and from their respective schools. They got rid of their old Essex and bought a brand-new black De Soto car.

During spare time, Pa planted fruit-bearing trees such as calamansi lemon, banana, santol, guava, caimito, and balimbing in their wide yard. "We will retain enough grassy space to play badminton in," said Pa. He and Ma had given up tennis and now played badminton with the kids. "And for our Christmas pageant. Our Christmas story must go on."

"Yes, tennis has become too strenuous for us," said Ma. "We're getting old."

"No, Ma, just say we prefer counting the leaves of trees," said Pa.

Pa loved trees. He often said he would have been a farmer had he not become a surgeon. Uncle John who often visited from Davao would boast about his own farm in Mintal. He, too, loved planting. After the two tired of talking about their plants, they would come around to the subject closest to their hearts, which was the main purpose of Uncle John's frequent visits to Manila — to set up a cancer research foundation, established by the Santos Cuyugan brothers. "Like the Mayo brothers clinic in the States, hah," they would say. "That's our dream, with our names written on it."

"I'd like to be your partner, too," Ceres butted in once while listening to their talk. "I'm going to study medicine in college. My dream is to be a doctor too — saving lives, saving and serving the sick and dying."

"Good, good!" said Uncle John. "Come join the company. We need you. What about Mario and Ruben? And Fides? Say, do you know, my eldest, we also named her Fides. But I don't know if she'd like to be a doctor, too. Her sisters, Madge and Verne, love dancing and singing. Guess what? Japanese songs!"

"Well, what can you expect, you live in a Japanese colony!" teased Ma.

Mintal was a suburb of Davao where Japanese businessmen had bought plantations of bananas, coconuts, and other crops, and settled their families there. It was like a piece of Philippine land owned and controlled by Japanese. The Japanese community had put up a school and a hospital and other centers of social services to serve its needs. Uncle John's family lived on this land. As director of the Mintal hospital he was a much respected member of the community.

Mario had graduated from high school and was now enrolled in an accounting course. Just as Pa had expected, the Arguelles's "iron hand" and Loging's sober and jolly companionship had worked wonders to straighten out Mario's sometimes lopsided priorities and propensity to go astray. Not reluctantly he came back to the fold when the family returned to the city and seriously pursued a career in the business profession. "Money talks," he often said. And he took very good care of his allowance money, saving up for the time, he said, when he would have to settle down and raise a family comfortably, "like our family," he would add.

Ceres, now in her teens, was about to graduate from high school. High school at PWU had been the best years of her school life. She had the best of classmates; no feeling of alienation bugged her now; she had rationalized and dismissed whatever differences each classmate showed in her way of thinking and living as inevitable, as part of one's family and social background and upbringing. She had finally accepted such differences. After all, there was no Deling, there were no unclad, poorly dressed, and malnourished girls here. They all belonged to the same social class. The differences lay in personal, trivial, less incomprehensible traits, characteristics, and peculiarities.

There were two groups in her class all the way to the senior year. One group called themselves, the Rinkydinks: they formed the

Camp Fire Girls. Ceres was one of the leaders of this group. They believed in life out-of-doors and spent week-ends pitching camp in each other's home yards. Their agenda did not include boys and dating—just plain fun making believe at survival away from home and old folks. Meanwhile the other group—the socialites and party-goers of the class—had begun dating boys and partying unchaperoned. One of them, Gloria Mapua, had just arrived from the States and came to class one day in full facial make-up, devilish-red lipstick and all. Miss Josefina Altiveros, the history teacher who was as ancient in dress, manner, and thinking as the pre-historic period she was teaching, almost fell off her chair, losing her usual rigid composure.

"No, no, no, Gloria, wipe off your make-up, you can't come to class like that!" she bellowed.

Gloria had to obey her, but after class she put it on again.

This group talked of nothing else but their 'dates.' The wonder of it all was, they were still tops in class.

Fides and Tem had joined the Girl Scouts and had proudly shown off their uniforms as members of such a big international organization, whose aim was to prepare young girls for the responsibility of good citizenship and wholesome living and service to the nation. They, too, with their group loved to go camping at the Girl Scouts Village, supervised by their troop leaders.

As for the music careers of the children, Ma had chosen the most well-known music teachers in town for Ceres, Ruben, and Fides. Mario had been scratched off her list of would-be musicians. He was no longer interested in music lessons. For Ruben, Ma bought a rare Stradivarius violin; for his violin professor, Ma chose the famous violinist Ernesto Vallejo.

Ceres was enrolled at the St. Scholastica's College of Music, for a music teacher's course. Every Thursday, she had to excuse herself from her high school classes at the PWU to attend classes at St. Scholastica in Harmony, History, Appreciation of Music, and piano lessons. Her teachers for the music courses were German Benedictine religious sisters who had such pristine voices when they sang hymns before each class, Ceres wondered if they were members of what Pa said were Hitler's Nazis conquering Europe. She had seen pictures in newspapers and magazines of congregations of nuns who had been convinced by Hitler to dream of *deutschland uber alles,* nuns singing *Deutschland uber alles und der welt* . . .. No wonder they were winning, Ceres thought, they were so intense looking, so full of vigor and zeal. Her piano teacher was Marcela Agoncillo, the daughter and namesake of the Filipina revolutionary who had sewn the first flag of the free Filipinas in 1898. How often Ceres would get a scolding from Miss Marcela when her rendition of Chopin or Beethoven did not express the slightest emotion. "Ceres!" the old lady would exclaim in her quaint British-Hong Kong accent, which she had acquired when the Agoncillos lived in exile in Hong Kong. "Why no passion, Ceres. It's because you have never suffered!"

It was Fides for whom Ma's dream of a musical career showed signs of becoming a reality.

"Yes, Ma, I shall be your dream come true. I shall not be like the Magill canaries. I shall be a nightingale, an *ibong adarna* bird, whose magical voice shall turn a stone to life!"

Even Felicing Tirona, the musical artist of the Tirona family of the PWU, was quick to notice Fides and promised to take her under her tutelage. "When the time comes, I shall be her teacher. Right now, she is too young, her voice is still changing," she had said.

Ruben was still at the Ateneo, an institution of the Society of Jesus where, under the tutelage of Jesuits, young boys were trained not only in strict Catholicism but also in collective community work and living. Ruben's unshakable thirst for knowledge could be equalled only by his mentors, the Jesuits. The pursuit and transmission of knowledge was his dream. Wherever he would go — to the far ends of the archipelago, from Aparri to Jolo, around the world, to the squatter hovels in the city, or to the nipa huts in the fields—he would teach people, the poorest of the poor, not chanting and prayer, but socialist-Jesuitical principles of equal distribution of wealth according to need, the dignity and worthiness of life, and love for humankind. Like his mentors, Ruben did not believe in contemplative life — he would remain in the world. He had told Pa he was going to the University of the Philippines, after Ateneo.

"Oh, don't tell me! You're going to U.P. because you're a Jesus-Hater!" teased Ceres. "Like the Jesuits, they are capable of anything, from the best to the worst of things."

"Say, what do you know! I read in history that the Jesuits were called Jesus-Haters, derogatorily. How'd you know that? Funny, hah!" said Ruben.

"You're going to U.P. to be with the heretics of U.P.," Ceres continued teasingly.

"No, to be with U.P.'s parish priest, Father Delaney, S.J., ha, ha!" Ruben laughed. "But seriously, I believe with all my heart, cross my heart, hope to die, the Jesuit Order's philosophy, 'To be all things to all men, so that they may be all things for all men!' There!"

War talk was still very much in the air and in the news. Hitler had become giddy with success in his drive to conquer Europe and dominate the world. "*Deutschland Uber Alles*" was incessantly played by musical instrumental bands in Germany, while Hitler in his shrill piercing voice would declare, "Our most prized possessions are our own people, the German people." He molded the minds and hearts of the German youth into a potent force in his formidable war machine. When a German declined to join his Nazi Party he was said to answer, "Never mind, we already have the souls and the future of your sons and daughters, you are already the past." His Nazis and Wehrmacht were marching, rolling, and flying all over Europe. The newspapers and radio screamed this news from across the seas.

Pa and Ma made it a point to follow all these events and discuss them with the children.

At Angelus, at table, and in church, Pa and Ma never failed to tell the children to include prayers for peace everywhere in the world.

"That is our collective dream," Pa said.

War!

*D*uring one of Uncle John's periodic visits with the family in Manila, he brought along his own family from Davao, Auntie Pilar and their seven daughters.

"It seemed like we'd never meet, like you live on another planet," Ma said to Auntie Pilar.

"It's because I'm so busy manufacturing babies, year after year, seven in eight years! Can you beat that!" Auntie Pilar laughed. She had a toddler and the last one, still very much a lap baby, and another one she was expecting in three months. "But we had to come now, or we might never meet and our children would be strangers to each other.

"Yes, just the other day our Fides, she sings, you know, was singing, 'Don't you go, don't you go to far Zamboanga.' Then she changed it to 'far away Davao, where you may forget your darling far away.'" Auntie Pilar chuckled. "I'm from Zamboanga, you know." Then seriously, she added, "But John will never forget his darling brother Gervasio, and their plans."

Then, the two mothers and homemakers compared their recipes for favorite dishes of the families. Auntie Pilar had learned Japanese cooking and she promptly showed off her own versions of *sushi*, *tempura*, and *sukiyaki* for dinner. Ma taught her the Bicol cooking of pork and vegetables with fresh coconut milk.

Pa and Uncle John held their private conversation in Pa's room. They talked of the war in Europe, dissecting the pros and cons of the possible involvement of the United States. Then, they moved to the dining room where they turned their mind and talk to something else—their project, the cancer research foundation. At the dining table, hunched over cups of coffee, they drafted the project study they would present to the state university, the U.P.

Ceres, Fides, and Tem invited some friends and classmates at school to meet their Davao cousins and held an instant jam session at home. It was meant to be an all-girls party but Mario and Ruben had some classmates around too.

"Aba, why leave us out?" asked Mario.

"Yeah, what's girls without us?" asked Ruben.

When they danced, the boys did not have to ask the girls. They all formed a circle and 'round and 'round they went: one, two, three, kick! one, two, three, kick! cha, cha, cha, cha! cha, cha, cha! went the samba cha-cha of Carmen Miranda and Xavier Cugat's phonograph music.

When the John Santos Cuyugan family bade good-bye to the Gervasio Santos Cuyugan family, they could not pull away from each other.

"We'll expect you again — when?" asked Ma.

"Ask John," said Auntie Pilar.

"Oh, you must come again with Uncle John," said Ceres to Auntie Pilar and her cousins, "Fides, Madge . . . all of you . . . We have such fun!"

"*Sayonara!*" said Fides of Davao.

"Wait, wait, first teach me one Japanese song, Fides," said Fides of Pasay to Fides of Davao.

"You better go to Davao and meet our Japanese friends there," said Madge.

"But it's so far away," said Fides. "We have to go by ship."

"We came here," said Madge.

Uncle John had to blow a whistle to call them away. "Ship ahoy! All aboard!"

After high school graduation, Ceres decided to go to the University of the Philippines. Mario and Ruben had dared her to apply for admission to the state university.

"Philippine Women's Ututin!" teased Mario in sing-song voice. "All you were taught at the PWU was dancing and dating and social etiquette, ha, ha! Low I.Q., full of air! You'll never get accepted at the U.P."

But Ceres made it. She enrolled for a preparatory medicine course, so she could pursue her childhood dream to be like Pa. She was doing fairly well. She met new girl friends and classmates: Ester Mapua, Ruby Roxas, the Jayme sisters, Emy Yuvienco, Letizia Roxas, Conchita Castillo, and many others.

One day out of the blue, a young man accosted Ceres as she was walking down the long corridor of Rizal Hall at the University and asked her to be his lady sponsor.

"What's that?" asked Ceres innocently, blushing to the tip of her nose. She had never heard of it before.

"You see, I'm a company captain of the ROTC," he replied.

"What's that? " Ceres asked again.

"Reserve Officers Training Corps. Every year, each officer chooses his girl to be like our muse, inspiration, our sponsor. May I ask you to be my sponsor?" he asked again.

Ceres was flattered but unconvinced. She didn't know what to say. She was unused to attention from boys. What if she failed to come up with what was expected of her? What if she didn't dress properly, didn't say the right words at the right time, didn't dance as she should? She felt she wasn't ready for that. She was totally unprepared for the requirements of such a role. She would be a completely raw recruit and would end up the laughing stock not only of the boys but of the girls as well, and of her brothers most of all.

She did not answer him until later, when he passed on notes to her in the girls' lounging room where her friends teased her to no end. He told her that his name was Frank Gomez, brother of Quintin, who was Pa's student.

"Quintin told me your pa is his favorite professor— he lectures not only about the anatomy of the body but about the country. And he always cracks jokes in class, even when the subject is life and death. That's why their class is always so lively."

"Oh yes," said Ceres, "my pa is like that. He doesn't want you snoring when he's lecturing."

So Frank and Ceres talked about Pa and Quintin. Also, she learned it was customary when asked, to readily accept, for it was a signal honor for a girl to be chosen a sponsor. She also learned that Letty Roxas would be the corps commander's sponsor, the most exalted one. Therefore, the limelight would be on Letty, not on her. Ceres did not want to draw attention to herself. She need not fear her inexperience.

Later a scandal sheet, which called the sponsors by derogatory names was plastered all over the walls of the U.P. building in campus: Letty was dubbed Olive Oyl because she was thin and slim like the cartoon character wife of Popeye the sailor man; Chitang Castillo was Miss-Hand-Me-Down because she wore dresses inherited from her older sisters; Ceres was Veronica Lake, the American movie actress with an identical hairstyle.

The suspected authors of the sheet were summoned to the President's office, so grievous was the crime and so destructive to the unsullied character of the targeted victims. Among those called were the naughty "porch lizards," so tagged because they were always hanging around the porch of Rizal Hall ogling the girls. They were Upsilon fraternity brothers: Corban Alabado, Delfin Villanueva, Rufino Valenzuela, Constante Cruz, Frank Quesada, and Eladio Adriano.

"How could I do that? I am about to court one of them!" protested Corban, who was feature editor of *The Collegian*, the university organ.

Nothing came out of the investigation as the unsigned sheets were distributed clandestinely. But Ceres never got over this wanton debasement of her integrity. To be accused of imitating an American was, to her, tantamount to treason. She promptly changed her long-tressed hairstyle, got a boy's bob, and never again grew her hair to one side.

U.P. was full of surprises for her. There were those monthly socials, "sexuals", the naughty porch lizards said they were, which were actually university dances under the supervision of Miss Ursula Clemente, the prim and proper Dean of Women. At the dance floor, the girls sat to one side of the social hall, the boys to another side or were standing against the walls. When the dance music played, the boys crossed over, properly introduced themselves to the girls and invariably asked for a dance. The girls had better acquiesce, stand up, dance, or be left sitting like wallflowers. No girl would risk that and forever be shunned as a KJ or killjoy. She would rather suffer the consequence of dancing with a totally boring bum, or if lucky, an entertaining bolero.

That was how Ceres met one of her tormentors, Corban. At one of those monthlies, he asked her for a dance. He was not a good dancer; he constantly stepped on her high-heeled shoes, but at least he was a sensible conversationalist. As a neophyte in U.P., she had so many questions to ask about the school; she learned a lot from him, and about him. He was a law student and had been in the university for four years. He also confided that very soon he expected to be conscripted into the army.

"It's my duty," he said. "There's a war going on, you know."

"Yes, but it's not here," Ceres said.

"No, but we're training for when it comes here," he said. "The university is the training ground not only for law, economics, government, health and science, medicine, technology, art, education, music, dance, all fields of endeavor, you name it we got it, but also for military service to our country and what's more, training for us citizens to be nationalists!

"Ooops, sorry," he muttered, as he almost stumbled on the floor. "Let's sit this one out, do you mind?"

"What do you mean, nationalists?" asked Ceres, as they walked to her seat.

"You know, you and me, everybody who loves his country and thinks only for the good of the country, for its interests, like our patriots, and heroes, dead or alive. Those are nationalists. Upholding democratic ideals. Like America. The U.P. stands for democracy and nationalism. After all, it's a state university, right? Financed by the state, by taxpayers, by your pa and mine."

"You talk like a lawyer."

"Shouldn't I?"

"You know, my pa talks like you too— but he's a doctor.

"Did he study here in U.P.?"

"No, but he teaches here and works here."

"See, see what I mean? U.P. Beloved . . . loyal thy sons we will ever be," and he began singing the U.P. hymn.

Everyone in the hall stopped dancing, those sitting stood up, and together they joined in the chorus of "U.P. Beloved."

Ceres and Corban began to see each other between class hours. After school, Corban and his brods (as the fraternity brothers called each other) would escort Ceres to her waiting De Soto car. He had shown her his desk at the Collegian office and she was impressed with his work in publications.

"Please come to my piano recital at Holy Ghost College,"

Ceres suddenly blurted out. "It's my joint junior graduation recital with Mercedes de Joya."

"Piano recital? You mean — you — ?" asked Corban, surprised.

"Yes, I love music, like my ma, my sister, brother. And oh, I'd like to invite you and your brods to my birthday party at the Wack Wack Golf and Country Club."

"Wack Wack! Wow, class! We'd love to go!" Then, he paused for a while. "But you know, I'm a poor man, and my friends are, well, they're not rich. Formal attire, coat and tie, is that required?"

Ceres shook her head.

"But your pa, he won't approve of us, he won't," Corban said.

"Yeah, yeah," joined in Delfin, Rufino, Didi, and Tante. "We won't be welcome."

"Dance?" asked Delfin.

Ceres stood to dance with Delfin. "It's all right. Come anyway, as you are, hah?" she said to them all.

Ceres' piano recital and birthday party came and went but her U.P. boy friends never showed up. Days and weeks passed without her seeing them. Perhaps, she guessed, they were having exams, and she promptly dismissed them from her thoughts.

It was nearing the Christmas season and, as in the years past, the Santos Cuyugan family was in a frenzy of preparations for the holidays— the pageant and gift-giving. There were as many indigent and handicapped children all around the neighborhood in Pasay.

But first, there were some mid-semestral exams the kids had to take before Christmas vacation. Mario was in his senior college year, Ruben in high school, Fides and Tem finishing elementary grades.

That day, December 8, Ruben, Tem, and Fides had no classes in their schools which were observing the Catholic holiday, the Feast of the Immaculate Conception. The state university and non-sectarian schools like Jose Rizal College, where Mario was enrolled for his business course, did not suspend classes for such a day.

As Ceres ran up the front steps of Rizal Hall and stepped onto the landing, the first thing that greeted her was a big blackboard blocking the way to the corridor, on which was scrawled in big bold letters: WAR! NO CLASSES!

Ceres was stunned.

"Hey, where's the picnic?" someone asked.

"Let's go!" the boys shouted.

Ceres told the family driver, Ciano, to drive back home. After Ceres had told them, Fides, Ruben, and Tem shouted,

"Yehey-y-y-y! Vacation!"

Call to Duty

*he zero hour has arrived. I expect every Filipino, man and woman, to do his or her duty. We have pledged our honor to stand to the last by the United States and we shall not fail her, happen what may."

Pa placed a radio on the breakfast table and listened to President Quezon's voice. Mario had arrived from school and all the children listened with Pa and Ma. More news reports and analysis were broadcasted over the radio repeatedly.

"The President of the United States, Franklin Delano Roosevelt, had sent a personal message to Emperor Hirohito of Japan to keep the peace in the Pacific. But Japan attacked Pearl Harbor in Hawaii, at 7:55 in the morning on December 7, and then Camp John Hay in Baguio, Clark Field at Fort Stotsenberg in Central Luzon. President Roosevelt has asked the American Congress to declare war on Japan.

" . . . Roosevelt nationalized Filipino forces under General MacArthur, commander-in-chief in the Far East who had been recalled earlier into the American Army. This new command of U.S. Army Forces include forces of the Commonwealth of the Philippines

called into service of the armed forces of the United States . . . .
Supplies have begun to flow into the Philippine military garrisons but
they have been slow and insufficient . . ."

Then President Quezon's voice came through again,

" . . . This will give us an opportunity before we finally sever the
ties that bind us with the United States in 1946 to show the Americans
that our gratitude to them for all the manifest blessings they have
brought to us is so deep-seated that we are willing and ready to lay
down our fortunes and our lives in its defense . . . it will teach our
youth that, reared in the ease and comfort of an American-protected
market, had whiled away its time in luxury and frivolity — how to
suffer and how to die. For no nation is worth anything unless it has
learned how to suffer and how to die."

"I will have to go to the hospital," Pa said. "Classes are suspended
but not hospital work."

"But Pa," protested Ceres. "They might bomb Manila, if they
could bomb Baguio."

"That's right. We'd better get some sandbags and make an air-raid
shelter," said Pa.

"Where, Pa, where?" asked Ruben.

"Here, under our porch," suggested Ma. "And we'll have to put
a portable toilet bowl there, just in case."

"And a can of crackers," Fides added.

Pa had left for the hospital when suddenly Mario heard the air-
raid siren wailing.

"Hey, do you hear that?" he asked. The next thing he heard was
the ominous drone of low-flying planes. He looked up to the sky.
"Hey, do you hear that? See that?" And he pointed upwards as he
craned his neck to look up from the porch.

Ma ran from the kitchen, followed by all the girls and Ruben.

"Are those our planes, or the enemy's?" asked Ceres.

"Stupid! The sirens warning us — that means they're enemy!"
said Mario.

"Let's not take chances," said Ma, as she urged all of them to take cover.

Not knowing where to take shelter, they ran to the wide spreading mango tree at the back of the house, as if the leaves and branches could stop the bombs. They ran around and around the tree, like trapped mice looking for a safe hiding hole. Then they realized how foolish they were. Still trembling from fear, they began to laugh. First Ma, then Mario, Ruben, and all the girls. They searched the sky for the planes. As suddenly as they had come, the planes were nowhere in the patch of sky they could see through the leaves. They never found out whether those were friendly or enemy planes, but thank God, Ma prayed, no bombs were dropped.

Later when Pa came back from the hospital, he said he too heard the planes.

"They are our planes patrolling our skies. The Japs won't dare come this way," he said.

"But they bombed John Hay and Clark . . ." said Ma.

"Only the American military bases," said Pa.

Two days later Pa had the sandbags delivered, and everyone helped build a temporary dug-out under the porch.

"There was a bit of news on the air that there was a bomb dropped somewhere in the suburbs, in Paranaque I think, and a residential house was a direct hit," Pa announced.

"Oh no!" gasped Ma.

"We didn't hear it on our radio," said Ceres.

"Yes, a whole family was killed. I didn't quite get the name. It sounded like Quiat," said Pa.

Ceres jumped up. "Oh no! I had a classmate by that name, on the party-goers' group, and she lives there!"

"Hurry, get our sandbags all piled up. It seems these Japs do not choose their targets," said Pa.

When the mailman came in the afternoon, there was a letter addressed to Ceres, postmarked San Marcelino, Zambales.

It was from her U.P. friend Corban. In the letter he said he and his U.P. brods had been drafted to active service two months ago, and were inducted into the USAFFE, the United States Armed Forces in the Far East. He was with the Infantry stationed in the jungles of Zambales. He wrote,

"Here, there is absolutely no electricity and running water. Drinking water is rationed to us once a day. But what impresses me here is the scenery and the wonders of nature, the mountain ranges and the primeval rain forests. From our barracks I can walk to a wide river bed, dry and sandy, dotted with fallen, decaying tree trunks all covered with outgrowths of wild orchids. If only I could pluck a dozen of them to send to you, I know you love to clip them to your hair. On the river banks grow tall trees overhanging with flowering vines and plants. I remember my father, he's a preacher, you know, in his reflections he'd say, we should be like trees growing on the banks of a river, getting sustenance from the river, which is like God. I would sit by the river bank under the trees and forget the hard military life I am living. Sometimes I get surprised or I surprise— I dunno who is the more surprised — some wild deer running under the trees. But all is not wonderful. Boy, the mosquitoes, how they bite, they abound here. We joke and say if we catch a basinful we can have pancakes of fried mosquitoes for breakfast.

"But at night my favorite spot is a lone kapok tree near my barracks. I watch myriads of fireflies flit in and out of its branches. Ceres, nothing in the world can beat the sight of a tree sparkling with a million tiny lights of the fireflies. Why, I already have a decorated Christmas tree! Merry Christmas to you — what do you want me to bring you: (1) pancake mosquitoes; (2) starlight fireflies; (3) just me, hah! All of the above or none of the above?"

Ceres smiled and sighed. So that was the reason for his non-appearance and long silence. But at the time of his writing, he had not known that war had finally come to the Philippines.

Mario too received a letter, a call to active duty from the army.

He hurriedly packed a few things: toothbrush, underwear, and a little notepad.

"I'll be back next week, Ma, don't worry," he said as he noticed Ma wipe away a tear. "This will only be a short war. See my muscle?" He flexed his arm muscles.

"What is this, a boxing bout?" asked Ruben.

Mario kissed everybody, and then he was off for somewhere down south in Laguna. "I shall join my group from school," he shouted, with a backpack on his back, as if he was going on a picnic.

There were rumors and rumors. Nobody knew what to think and believe. Radio broadcasters were advising listeners to keep calm, not to believe everything they heard. But on December 12, it was no longer a rumor that President Quezon and General MacArthur held a conference to discuss the necessity of evacuating to Corregidor, an island fortress at the entrance of Manila Bay.

President Quezon was adamant, the radio broadcaster related, and at first refused to go with MacArthur.

" 'But why? It never crossed my mind that there would ever come a time when I had to go to Corregidor. I am no American Governor General but the Filipino President of the Commonwealth. Why should I go to Corregidor? My people will think I am abandoning them to seek safety for myself under your protection. This I shall never do. I shall stay with my people and suffer the same fate that may befall them.' "

"But MacArther said it was his duty to prevent Quezon from falling into enemy hands, as if the government had not been captured or surrendered. Thus, President Quezon was in a dilemma—to continue in office to help alleviate the suffering of his people or to avoid collaboration to preserve the integrity of Philippine values and institutions."

Events were moving so fast. Pa and Ma kept the radio on all day so they could hear more news. The newspapers and the radio reported running accounts of the conduct of the war:

"On December 22, the Japanese landed in Lingayen Gulf; on December 23, on Lamon Bay, south of Manila. It is a pincer operation to surround Manila. MacArthur ordered the complete withdrawal of all Filipino-American forces to Bataan. General Wainwright was ordered to hold the bridge at Calumpit, north of Manila, until all of the Filipino-American troops had passed. There was no more time for rational discussion and consultation with the Philippine government authorities. MacArthur is in full command.

"Today before Christmas eve, Quezon met his Cabinet and Council of State in full attendance for the last time. It was a poignant farewell meeting. Quezon was taking along with him only a skeleton staff: Vice-President Sergio Osmena, Chief Justice of the Supreme Court Jose Abad Santos, and General Basilio Valdez, his aide-de-camp . . ."

"Isn't Abad Santos your relative, Pa?" asked Ceres.

"Shhhh, yes, listen," said Pa.

"One of those he was leaving behind to take care of Manila was his Executive Secretary Jorge Vargas. To him Quezon's instruction was: 'Protect the civilians. Perform neutral functions, municipal and administration of justice.' When Jose Laurel asked: 'What shall we do if the Japanese asked us to do things inimical to Philippine or American government?' Quezon replied: 'What can you do under the circumstances? You have to do what they expect you to do except one thing — taking an oath of allegiance to Japan. What is acceptable, what is treasonable? Each of you, as Filipino leaders, has the lonely task of determining your own set of values.' "

In the afternoon a letter came in from Mario. Pa and the kids gathered around Ma who read it aloud, her voice trembling, her hands shaking:

"Dear Pa and Ma and family,
I am under the command of General Vicente Lim, your
friend, Pa and Ma. We have been ordered to go to Bataan.
Don't worry, they say it's the safest place in the world. Not too

far away from you, down south. You can see me from the Bay. I'm all right. I miss you all. Especially now that it's almost Christmas. Shall we have Christmas? If I have to give up my life—it's too bad I have only one to give—I would gladly give it. That's my gift to you all."

Open City

Let's prepare for our Christmas," said Ma.

"But Mario is not here," protested Ceres.

"We're not family," said Fides.

"What's Christmas without family?" asked Ruben.

"He's here in spirit, if not in flesh," said Pa.

"Besides Christmas is not only for our family, but for children—all children. We've invited the children," said Ma. Then she added, "And I've bought — guess what — pencils for them, plus our calamansi fruits. Now get busy and pack them up in our little brown bags."

"Rain or shine, war or peace, the show must go on," said Pa.

"The Babe Jesus is born," said Ma.

Then Fides remembered. "What about us, we have no gifts to each other. Me, I have none."

"Don't say that," said Ma. "Pray for a miracle. If we survive, that's the greatest gift we can receive and we'll know it's directly from Baby Jesus."

The Santos Cuyugan family pushed through their Christmas pageant and gift-sharing amidst the turmoil of war and the uncertainty of tomorrow. The children of the neighborhood came, the Three Kings passed through, and most of all, Jesus was born in the manger. Never had the angels, shepherds, kings, sheep, and all the animals sung Joy to the World more fervently and hopefully, as the stars shone ever so brightly above them.

Finally on Christmas day, General MacArthur declared Manila an "open city." He declared a scorched-earth policy. The last remaining Filipino-American troops in the city ignited everything which could be of value to the enemy, or which they could not move. For days, the burning oil dumps blanketed the city with a thick black fog. At night the city was a jungle of fire, with the sky all lit up.

"It's like daylight, so bright and hot," said Ceres.

"Merry Christmas! Merry Christmas!" shouted Ruben.

"What a waste of oil," said Ceres.

"Better than it's going to the enemy," said Ruben.

"Why not give to us?" asked Ceres.

"No time," said Ruben.

"Yes, it's Christmas time for gift-giving," said Ceres.

Then the family heard over the radio that people had plunged onto opened warehouses of the American Army and then into unopened warehouses of private business firms. They had a happy field day looting whatever they could carry or load into a vehicle. Many of them, observed the broadcaster, were poor homeless squatters and scavengers of the city. For them it was indeed a Merry Christmas they'd never had before.

The radio broadcaster speculated that the Japanese would be entering the city on New Year's Eve. The city waited with bated breath. Hardly any cars were on the street, except Pa's. He said he had to go to the hospital, no matter what happened. Then on the day before the Eve, Pa decided to evacuate the family to the Abad Santos residence on Taft avenue, across the Philippine Women's University. It was a gloomy cold damp day with just a hint of rain in the air.

"We'll move tonight as soon as it's dark, so we won't attract attention," Pa said. "You never can tell about those Jap soldiers. We have three young girls. You'll be safe there with proper protection. I've talked with Indang Manda. "

The Abad Santoses were relatives of Pa. More than that, his patients too. So was Pedro Abad Santos, the brother, who was the founder of the Socialist Party which had gone underground because it had been declared illegal. It had aligned itself with the Communist Party and the Hukbalahap, Hukbo Laban sa Hapon, Huk for short (the People's Anti-Japanese Army). It had accused the Nacionalista Party, the party in power, to be a tool of American imperialism, whose aim was to exploit weak and small nations like the Philippines. Pa had explained this to the children but he had not brought them close to these contrasting Abad Santoses: Jose as Chief Justice of the Supreme Court was with the government, and Pedro with an outlawed political party. Now, Pa said, he was offered temporary dwelling in a government-protected home.

"But, Pa, shall we not be imposing on them?" asked Ma.

"Oh no, Indang Manda called me to bring you there. There are only the three girls and Ossie. Cacang Jose brought his son Pepito with him to Corregidor. The more the better in their house, she said. Only for a few days till we know how the Japs will behave when they enter the city," said Pa.

Reluctantly, Ma agreed to move the children to the Abad Santos house. Pa stayed home. That night Ma and Indang Manda ordered all the windows and doors of the house closed and securely bolted.

"No peeping out of the windows, girls," Indang Manda ordered. "Remember, you must not be seen by the Japs."

Close to midnight, while the children were fast asleep, a faint creaking sound of opening and closing of a door, followed by some light hurried footsteps, then whisperings, half-awakened Ma. She listened closely, but could not make out who was talking or about what.

The next morning, Indang Manda confided to Ma that her eldest son, Pepito, had secretly slipped into the house in the middle of the night under cover of pitch darkness, to deliver a message from his father in Corregidor to his mother — for her not to worry about him and Pepito, that he would be going with the President to the south, to the Visayas to set up the Philippine government. They would ride a submarine. No one must know this secret for security reasons, her son Pepito had warned her.

Ma shivered. She was not used to such fearful secrets. Indang Manda had told her that she was used to that. Pedro Abad Santos, because he was wanted and operated underground, often shared secrets with her. She had practiced keeping confidential information, she said.

All around was quiet. There was not a sound, none of the merrymaking of the first day of the New Year. No one was astir. Manila had become a ghost town, so scared were the people to venture out of their homes to see, much less to greet, the new conquerors of their city.

The Abad Santos girls— Luz, Mandy, and Vicky — with Ceres, Fides, and Tem, were sorely tempted to take a peek, just a quick, tiny peek through a slit of the window facing Taft Avenue, a main thoroughfare. Ruben and Ossie kept away, not daring to disobey orders. The girls took turns. At first Luz and Mandy saw groups of two or three Japanese soldiers scattered all over the length of Taft Avenue, fronting the house, in full battle gear with camouflaged leaves on their heads. Fides saw some sitting squat on the pavement or the curb, eating from what looked like a tin plate. What was it, a small heap of rice, she guessed. Tem said some others were standing guard, at attention, looking nowhere.

Then, when it was Ceres and Vicky's turn, Ceres said she saw truckloads of troops — five, six, seven — she counted, an endless convoy of trucks loaded with soldiers. "Wow! They're so many!" she whispered.

"No, look, there's only two trucks, they're just going round and round in circles, hah!" said Vicky, as she strained her neck to follow the route of the two trucks turning the corner of the block, then back again, again, and again.

Ceres laughed. "They think they can fool us, ha, ha, ha!"

Indang Manda caught them red-handed.

"No, no, no, close that window! What did I tell you!" she cried.

"They're there! They're there! Keep quiet."

The girls rushed to the kitchen and spent the whole day and days after, baking cookies and biscuits. The Abad Santos girls were very efficient cooks, like their mother. Then they gorged on what they cooked all day. There was nothing else to do but to eat and live. They must continue to live.

Soon enough, a semblance of calm and order had descended upon the city. People started to go out into the streets, ignoring the Japanese soldiers posted everywhere. Until an order was issued from above, the military or the civilian government, no one seemed to know, that people should bow low to the soldiers as a sign of greeting and respect to them, or else suffer a stiff penalty. The penalty, Ciano discovered when he haughtily defied the order, was a slap right on one's face.

"Never mind," said Ciano. "Why should I bow to them? Who are they?" And he vowed never to pass in front of them again, ever.

A week passed before Pa decided it was relatively safe for his family to return home. He and Ciano fetched them in the car. After some tearful good-byes and thank-yous to the Abad Santoses, they all promised they would get in touch with each other for any important messages or news. Ciano took to the side streets, carefully avoiding sentries stationed at random posts on the streets.

Once more the family gathered together at home, each one with a prayer to the Christ Child that "Peace reign on earth, goodwill to all."

Short Wave Radio

Pa could no longer keep a deep secret he had been harboring for over a week while his family had been away. He waited until it was almost dark, after the Angelus, to reveal it.

First, he instructed Ruben to stand watch at the entrance iron-grilled gate. "Just stand there and see that no one, but no one, comes in or looks through, understand?" he whispered.

Then he led the rest to Tem's room. Tem's bed had been transferred to Fides' bedroom. "You are now to share your bedroom, Fides, with Tem. We shall need this room," Pa said to Fides.

They all crowded into the room and saw a small radio, not their ordinary one, but a more powerful one, Pa said. Then he turned a knob and a voice with impeccable American English accent came on the air:

"American relief convoy is on the way. General Douglas MacArthur is holding the fort. The Japanese cannot win. American reinforcements are coming. The American fleet will come and rescue. . . MacArthur has said, 'The Japanese have the bottle, but we have the cork.'"

Pa turned it off. "Call Ruben." When Ruben came, he said, "The Japs have prohibited the people from listening to any broadcast of American origin of any news against Japan. On January 3, the Japanese commander-in-chief issued a proclamation announcing the demise of the sovereignty of the United States over the Philippines and of martial law over the districts the Army has occupied. That all our laws except those against Japanese interests will be all right, will continue in force, such as freedom of religion and residence. That the purpose of the Japanese is to liberate the Filipinos from the oppressive domination of America. The Philippines for the Filipinos, Asia for Asians. Establish the Greater East Asia Co-Prosperity Sphere, the *Dai-Toa Kyoeiken*. Assert yourselves as Orientals, said the proclamation.

"So now we are under martial law," Pa ended his speech.

"What's that?" asked Ruben.

"Under the military rule of the Japanese," Pa continued. "We have to obey and believe whatever they say. But of course, we are not stupid, we don't have to believe everything. For example, they require all radios to be turned in to them. They want to be sure, no short wave radios like this. No American propaganda. If you're caught, you die. That's why I say, we have to be very, very conscious of this. No talking to anyone about this, understand?"

"What about Ciano?" Ma asked.

"I think he can be trusted. Tell him about it," said Pa. "You tell him, Ma. He can come listen, too."

Everyday Pa and the family continued to listen to their clandestine short wave radio. "It is our only contact with the outside world," Pa said.

Once they came upon a Filipino-accent speaking voice on the air describing how President Quezon, upon learning of the "Europe First Policy" of the United States, blew his top and addressing the United States said, " 'This war is not of our making. We decided to fight by your side, but how long are we going to be left alone?

Has any government the right to demand loyalty from its citizens beyond its willingness or ability to render actual protection? America writhes in anguish at the fate of a distant cousin, Europe, while a daughter, the Philippines, is being raped in the back room . . . Since no aid is forthcoming while America helps other nations . . . we are practically doomed to total extinction. I urge a total withdrawal of both the Japanese and American armed forces . . . We must try to save ourselves, and to hell with America!'"

Pa was visibly affected by this outburst of Quezon.

"He has finally realized the futility of aligning our country with any foreign power," Pa said.

"Yes," said Ma. "How sad he sounds and must feel. Why doesn't he return to Manila?"

"But he's a sick man," said Ceres. "Pa said he has TB. How can he fight the Japs?"

"The other leaders he left behind are not fighting the Japs. The Japs said they will also give us independence, they will not kill us," said Ma.

"But what kind of independence, we don't know. Quezon is right, we must stand by ourselves, to hell with all foreign powers who want to control and dominate us!" said Pa.

The next news they heard over the radio was that General MacArthur, President Quezon, and Vice-President Osmena had escaped by PT boat to Australia. They were on their way to Washington, D.C. The voice kept repeating the assurance that "American relief convoy is coming . . . General MacArthur has said, 'I shall return.'"

"But when?" asked Ceres.

"Ask MacArthur. I forgot, he's gone, with Quezon and Osmena," said Ruben.

"What about Abad Santos, his name was not mentioned?" asked Ceres.

Pa contacted Indang Manda but there had been no message, she said. No news about him.

Three weeks later, a rumor went around that Abad Santos had been captured by the Regional Military Commander in the Visayas. He had refused to pledge allegiance to Japan and was executed. That he had said to his son Pepito who was with him: "Son, do not be sad. This is a rare opportunity for me to die for our country. Not everybody is given that chance." Pepito's whereabouts were unknown.

"But those are just rumors," said Ruben.

Pa had a faraway look. "Most likely they're true," he said.

Then on April 9, the grave and solemn voice of Norman Reyes of the Voice of America over the radio announced: "Bataan has fallen. The spirit is willing, but the flesh is weak. It is no match to sword and steel . . . "

"Oh my God!" exclaimed Ma, bursting into tears. "What's going to happen to our boys over there? To Mario?"

Pa wrapped his arms around her. "There's nothing we can do but pray. Mario is a sturdy one, Ma. He can take care of himself. "

The radio continued to broadcast news from the front.

"While the guns of Bataan have been silenced with the surrender of the Filipino-American forces to the Japanese, the island fortress of Corregidor is now the target of Japanese bombardments. So intense is the attack with artillery and bombs that it seems the people of Manila can hear the explosions. The brave Filipino-Americans in the fort have vowed to fight to the last man, until they are ordered by General Wainwright to surrender to General Homma, the commanding general of the Japanese Imperial forces."

Another pall of gloom descended upon the city.

"If the Americans cannot protect us, what about our leaders?" asked Ruben. "The Americans say we're cockroaches. Survivors, since the beginning of time, but stupid!"

"And if our leaders cannot protect us, what about us, why don't we fight?" asked Ceres. "For our honor, if not for our lives!"

"With what?" asked Pa in turn. "It isn't easy. I heard from our Pampanga relatives, the Huks — haven't I told you about them? —

they are farmers, laborers, and some intellectuals and professionals, they are fighting. And then there is the Socialist Party of Cong Perico Abad Santos, and the Communist Party, and many other guerrillas — the Hunters, Marking, ROTC, Ramsey, the ECLGA, Fertig — I don't know many of them — shhhh — don't talk about them. They are fighting in the hills and mountains, underground, in towns and cities, fighting and dying," explained Pa.

But life had to go on. Pa reported for work at the hospital, day after day. News blacked out from the front. None of the Filipino leaders in government could tell the mothers and fathers of the fighting men and women in Bataan and Corregidor the fate that had befallen their loved ones. The least that could be done for them, Ma, Pa, and all these other mothers and fathers bewailed, was to let them know — were their loved ones still alive?

Death March

The Manila newspapers taken over by the Japanese from the Roces family, *The Manila Tribune*, *La Vanguardia*, and the *Taliba*, hardly carried any news about the fighting sons and daughters of Bataan and Corregidor. Nor did the short wave radio. The Santos Cuyugan family was getting jittery. Ma wanted to go to Bataan to look for her son Mario.

"It's no use, Ma." Pa dissuaded her from such a plan. "You won't find him that way. Let's wait for some developments."

"Wait? Until he has become a corpse rotting in the jungles?" cried Ma.

"No, no, he's alive. I know he's alive!" Pa assured her. Ma was beginning to lose weight. She refused to eat. Pa was getting more worried about her and was on the brink of giving in to her and letting her go with Ciano and Ruben as bodyguards. They would take the bus. The car could no longer be used, as gasoline had been rationed only to high government officials and the Japanese. Pa had to take any available transporation to and from the hospital. Sometimes he walked or hitched a ride with a neighbor who had ingeniously devised a horse-drawn carriage like a *calesa*, but bigger, and called it a *do-kar*. Many such so-called *do-kars* were now on the streets. "Hey, you know," said Pa, "when I was small, we used to have quiles, it was called then — like the *calesa*, now the *do-kar*." And Ruben asked, "Quiles, calesa, do-kar, what will it be next?" Tem replied, "Cadillac-*lakad!* (walk)"

One day, a middle-aged man stood at their gate.

"Yes?" Pa shuffled to the gate and peered at his face.

The man spoke in Kapampangan, the Pampanga dialect, "I'm Victoriano Alabado, father of Corban. Your daughter Ceres, I understand, is a friend of my son in U.P. He has a message for her. Oh, by the way, I am a Reverend Pastor of a Christian Methodist Church . . . "

"Come in, come in. Ceres!" Pa called.

Ceres had never met him before and was pleasantly surprised to see him. Her heart was beating fast, wondering why he came. Was it news about Corban? Was he alive? But if he was dead, how did his father get the address of her home? Why did he come at all? Did Corban leave a message on his dead body? All these questions raced around in her mind.

Speaking in English to Ceres, he explained his mission. Ma came forward. Ciano, Ruben, and Tem were all ears too.

"I saw Corban in Lubao. You know we live in Lubao, Pampanga, and after I learned that our soldiers in Bataan had surrendered and were marching on the road from Bataan to Pampanga, and God knows where," he paused. "I watched on the road for hours, for days, not leaving the spot where I stood, except once in a while, to help out a fallen soldier and to give water and *panotsa*, you know, caked molasses. I stood there watching out for Corban."

"What about M . . . " Ma was about to ask for Mario, but bit her lip when she realized he didn't know him.

"Yes, Ma'am?" asked Rev. Alabado.

"My son, Ceres' older brother, Mario, he's there too," said Ma.

"Oh is that so? I can tell you this, Ma'am," he said, assuring her. "While some of the boys look weak and starved, others seem to be still strong and able to take it. In fact, when I finally saw my son and I tried to convince him to escape with me, as our house is not too far away from the road where they were marching, he said, 'No, Tatang, look, I'm still good for many more kilometers.' He refused to go with me. It's too risky, he said, he'd seen the Japs bayonet his comrades who tried to go out of the line, right before his eyes, and not only his comrades but also their saviors, fathers, mothers or whoever tried to save them. And anyway, Corban had said, they were going to be set free.

"And here is what else he told me. You see, there was a pause in the march, I was able to talk with him for a few minutes. This is his story:

"'You know what, Tatang, when we were told to surrender, we dumped our guns and ammunitions into the sea. My squad and I came upon a huge pile of boxes of food supplies left by the Americans who were no longer around — you see the Americans were the ones in charge of the supplies, they just gave us a ration of a can or two of sardines per day — well, we thought we hit the jackpot! There I was sitting on top of this pile when I was spotted by Taka, you know Takahashi, he used to operate a small refreshment stand near the railroad station in San Fernando . . .'

"Yes, I remember him, I said to Corban, interrupting him." Then Rev. Alabado continued to relate Corban's story.

"'Well, Taka saw me and called out to me, Corban, Corban! I was surprised to see him. At first I thought he was one of us until I saw he was in the civilian uniform of the Japanese, khaki cap with a star and white band in Japanese characters, and a saber, yes, he had a saber. He spoke in Kapampangan, and he told me and my squad to get as much food as we could carry because we had to walk to Balanga, no transportation, and from Balanga to San Fernando. So I ordered my men to get sugar, canned goods, anything to eat.

We had so much, we ate as we walked, even giving away some on the way.

"'Before Taka and I parted, I asked him, What will they do to us? And he smiled and said, You are not the enemy. You are only misguided. It is the white people who are our enemies. We will only take you to a registration point, list your names, then let you go. So don't worry.

"'After that I never saw him again. So, Tatang, don't worry, we will be released maybe in San Fernando. And go tell Ceres, I can't write her, just tell her what I told you. I'm here safe and sound with lots of food. This is her address.'"

Pa and Ma could not quite believe Rev. Alabado's story but it was good to hear it, they sighed with relief. They offered him dinner and then asked him to stay for the night.

"I have to leave early tomorrow morning to meet those boys in San Fernando," Rev. Alabado said. And to Ma, he added, "I'll see if I can find your son Mario, Ma'am. I'll come back as soon as I have some news again."

"Yes, yes, please do," Pa and Ma said.

In a week's time, Rev. Alabado was back, his face ashen and haggard, for the sad tale he had to narrate.

It turned out that what Takahashi told Corban were all lies. The march was a death march, not only because of the cruelty of the Japanese, but also because of the most severe physical conditions the boys had to suffer. They marched with new GI-issued ill-fitting, but classy-looking, leather combat shoes, which they wore to show off to loved ones they expected to be reunited with soon. But the shoes gave them such painful foot sores and calluses, they had to take them off, and endure barefooted the searing heat of the asphalt or rough dirt road under the scorching sun for hours and hours. It seemed endless. When they ran out of food, they became so thirsty that their parched lips cracked with the intense heat. Some dared break out of the line to quench their thirst in a roadside artesian well gushing clear cool water, and were instantly bayonetted or shot by their guards. *Kura! Kura!* were the last words they would hear. Those who had fallen by the wayside, unable to take another step, were kicked by stone-hard boots, and bayonetted for failure to respond and obey orders to go on. Sometimes in the warehouse in Lubao where they spent the night, packed like cards standing upright, the Japanese soldiers would, for no reason at all, yank out those who were standing by the entrance door or crouched on the ground asleep, and ruthlessly, mercilessly beat them to death.

When they finally reached San Fernando, instead of being released as Taka had assured Corban, they were herded into fully enclosed railroad freight trains called boxcars — narrow-gauge boxcars made of steel, thirty-feet long, eight-feet across, seven-feet high, or boxcars made of wood, smaller, and a foot shorter in height. Groups of one hundred or as many as could be squeezed in, were herded into these boxcars for a slow ride that would take an agonizing three hours to Capas, Tarlac. Just a tiny slit between the sliding doors provided some life-giving air. But for many who could not reach out for that wisp of air, death by suffocation was the only total relief.

By the time the train pulled over at the station and the doors of the death trap were finally opened, those who miraculously survived rushed out over the dead bodies of their comrades. Piles and piles of bodies on top of each other were brought out and mercifully laid on the ground for all the world to witness.

This was what Rev. Alabado witnessed. He had followed the march to Calvary, to the concentration camp of O'Donnell in Capas, Tarlac, unable to convince his son to escape, unable to see him anywhere later on, dead or alive.

Capas

I'll go, I'll go with you to Capas, Rev. Alabado," Ma
declared determinedly. "No one's going to stop me now."
"Yes, Ma'am," said Rev. Alabado. "My wife, Miling, can also no
longer wait for news. She is going to Capas to look for her son
herself. You can go together."

There was still more disheartening news. General Vicente Lim
had been killed.

"Why, our friend General Lim, isn't he Mario's commanding
general in his outfit? Didn't he say so in his letter? Oh my God,
where is he, where," and Ma repeated and repeated a hundred times,
"I'm going, I'm going, if they have to kill me too."

Pa no longer had the heart to object to Ma's decision.
Ma, Ruben, Miling, and Rev. Alabado went together to Capas.

They rented a small nipa hut at the outskirts of the town where
the camp was. Many more families, fathers and mothers, followed
suit, renting rooms in areas surrounding the camp. Everyday they
watched the Japanese sentries changing guard at the entrance gate,
hoping and praying to see a friendly-looking one they could talk to,

perhaps ask about their sons if they were inside, perhaps to allow them to go inside for just a short while, maybe offer a *puto seco,* a Pampanga delicacy. Before they could firm up their strategy, Rev. Alabado had gone ahead and pretending to be a carpenter, volunteered to the Japanese authorities to help in the makeshift construction inside the camp.

"I help, free," he said. "Have tools, carpenter."

The Japanese reluctantly accepted his offer and so he gained access to the camp. Day after day he went in with his pack of tools. He became one of the very few Filipinos who could go in and out of the camp. He became the envy of the rest of the fathers and mothers waiting outside, still hoping by all means fair and foul to get inside or at least hand a letter through to loved ones. It was a test of one's resourcefulness and diplomatic savvy to talk oneself in or get a message through. In no time Rev. Alabado became the conduit of news from inside and outside, letters passing through him. He was no longer the envy but the most sought-after to deliver messages. He was the bringer of news, good or bad, to the crowd outside. Not only the news communicator but also the chronicler of all that he would witness in camp and out.

The camp was so congested there was no room to separate the sick, the dying, and the dead. Men were starving. They were getting sick of dysentery, cholera, flu, malaria, pneumonia, beriberi, all kinds of communicable diseases. They were dying like flies, sometimes five hundred a day. The situation finally alarmed the Japanese themselves who feared the condemnation of the whole world for the wanton slaughter of these prisoners of war. The Command ordered a system devised to gather needed food, herbs and medicines, and fetch water. The prisoners organized themselves: ten able-bodied ones to compose a group to go out of the camp to scrounge around for anything that was edible or medicinal, accompanied by a Japanese guard. One such group was called the "guava detail," which gathered guava fruits, leaves, branches, bark of the tree. Guava was said to be good to stop diarrhea and cure dysentery. There was the banaba detail, water detail, burial detail. Any "detail" to use as an excuse to go out and see the crowd outside, throw a written message, perchance to be delivered by the finder to the one it was addressed to.

At last Rev. Alabado had the best news for Ma. He had seen and met Mario and had told him to join the guava detail.

"Tomorrow, Ma'am, he will go out, they will be brought over there," and he pointed to a guava orchard nearby. "You and Ruben, be there, you'll see him, perhaps you can talk to him. If the guard says no, don't insist. Just wave to him."

"Yes, yes," said Ma, so happy was she. She whispered, "Thank God."

"As for you, Miling, I have not seen Corban inside. Nobody could tell me if he had been seen anywhere, any time," said Rev. Alabado.

It was Miling's turn to cry.

"But don't lose hope. Pray," Rev. Alabado patted her. Then he added, "Tomorrow I'm going to Manila to relay the news to Doctor Cuyugan."

"Please do," said Ma. "And tell Ceres and the girls to prepare whatever they can — food and medicines — for you to bring back here for the boys in camp. Don't forget, hah, please. Those poor boys need food. Tell Ceres to be in charge."

Rev. Alabado waited for the guava detail the next day before leaving for Manila. He wanted to be sure Mario would be in it so he and his mother would at least see each other. And they did. But they couldn't get anywhere near each other. Ma waved her hand and Mario waved back.

Again Ma told Rev. Alabado, "Tell the Doctor, Mario is all right. He doesn't seem to be sick, does he? Tell the Doctor, hah? And don't forget the food and medicines."

Rev. Alabado reached Manila and Pasay before nightfall and the family received him with such warmth for the good news he brought them. After dinner, he rattled off some names of the prisoners he had seen alive inside. He had a list of those he had not seen that relatives had asked for, and after their names he drew a cross sign to indicate that they were missing or might have died. One of them was his son Corban.

When Ceres saw this, her heart sank. She had been looking

forward to seeing him again. She recalled their happy encounters during those monthly socials at the U.P.; his meeting her after class to escort her to her car; the naughty and mischievous pranks he and his brods played on the girls, the professors, and even the Deans; his story about how a certain Upsilon brod by the name of Ferdinand Marcos initiated him into the fraternity by kicking him hard in his butt. She could feel warm blood rush to her face, but she felt cold. Was she falling in love with this man who could now be dead? Her hand touched Rev. Alabado's hand at the table.

"Please look for him," she said.

"I shall continue to look for him. Maybe I just have not been lucky," said Rev. Alabado. "Will you be ready with some food I could bring to Capas, maybe tomorrow?"

"Oh yes, yes," said Ceres. It was the least she could do for those hungry, sick, and dying boys. Who was it who said 'they also serve who only stand and wait'? Well, she would do more than wait.

Ceres took charge. She mobilized everyone in the house to prepare the food and medicines. The household became a relief agency. Adela and Maria, and the Arvisu family on their occasional visits with the family, were on hand and offered to help in cooking and packing everything. Ciano, grounded as he was with the car, helped out too.

First, they decided who would be the master cook. Adela was the choice. She asked all the questions, chose the best answers, and supervised the cooking from then on. What food to prepare? Better prepare ready-to-eat food like bread and biscuits, crackers for diarrhea. Was there a big cooking pot? Use the *kawa*. What would go with the crackers? Jam — pineapple, papaya jam. Pinapaya jam.

"Go to the market," she ordered all the girls, "buy hundreds of pineapple and papaya, they're in season. And a sack of brown sugar. Ciano, go help them."

When all the ingredients were ready and the big cooking pot *kawa* brought out from storage, Adela yelled out new instructions:

"Okay, peel those fruits and cut them into cubes. Ciano, bring out the giant *kawa* into the yard — that's where we'll cook — under the mango tree. Start up a fire. Then, dump all the fruit pieces and sugar into the *kawa* with just enough water to stir the mash. We have to make the jam thick enough so we could cut it up and pack the pieces into cellophane wrappers. They can be eaten piece by piece like candy."

Stirring the mash as it thickened was easier said than done. Ceres designated Ciano the official "stir boy" but when she saw that he was slowing down, beads of perspiration all over his face, she asked everyone to give him a hand, take turns stirring. At last the thick mash was laid out in a big platter to cool, cut up into small pieces, wrapped in cellophane packs, and dumped into baskets.

Ceres had assigned Pa as the "medicine man." He came home not only with medicines — packs of sulfathiazole, quinine, aspirin, iodine, mercurochrome — bandages, and gauze, but also with cans of biscuits and soda crackers.

"Ciano," Pa ordered, "go with Rev. Alabado. Help him carry all these to Capas."

Every week since then, Rev. Alabado would come to relay news from Capas and get pinapaya jam, medicines, and other supplies for the prisoners in camp.

The Japanese soon enough got suspicious of his coming and going with such a loadful of things. At one point, they accused him of being a merchant of goods and medicines. His tool kit was inspected; luckily, he had already delivered the letters and foodstuff. He was investigated but he just laughed off the whole thing.

"I should be rich by now, but my God, I still haven't found my son."

A New Battle

Ma came home with Ruben after three weeks in Capas. It was enough, for the time being, to have seen Mario. There was nothing else to do but wait for his release. There were rumors that the Filipino prisoners would be released soon.

Jorge Vargas who had been left behind by President Quezon had been appointed Executive Commission Chairman by the Japanese Imperial forces. At a luncheon in honor of Commandant Colonel Ito Shiro of the Capas concentration camp, Vargas praised Colonel Ito as a friend and benefactor of the Filipino people, and that by his kindness and considerate treatment of the Filipino prisoners of war, he had won the support and admiration of the Filipino people. Then he issued an order that no person should visit the war prisoners' camp or exert efforts to intercede on behalf of any prisoner.

"Ha! Ha!" sneered Ruben. "As if we will obey that order! Can he not see how many of us were there looking for our brothers, husbands, fathers, sons, boyfriends? How blind can he be?

"And if he only knows how Rev. Alabado fools those Jap sentries," Ruben continued. "How the prisoners themselves fool them too — with those detail-detail tricks. They go all over town, not just the surrounding area, pretending to look for more guava, bananas, water — why, if not for those armed guards, they could have wandered as far away as here! We have guava trees here! Ha, ha!" Ruben laughed.

"Yeah, this government, our government is a fool! Why doesn't it open its eyes? Wise up, open its mind! See that the people are not stupid, they cannot be fooled!" said Ceres.

"Yes," agreed Ma. "Why doesn't our government do something for the people for once. Forget the Japanese aid and promises, forget the American aid and promises — independence, freedom, promises, promises. We have to fight for it ourselves! Look what's happening to our children!"

"Now, now, calm down, you three. Let's give President Quezon — our Commonwealth government-in-exile — a chance. Let's wait. Continue to hope," said Pa.

The three simmered down in a while. There was work to do.

It was the season for the calamansi to fruit. They had to be gathered and sent to camp with the pinapaya jam and medicines. Rev. Alabado would be coming for them soon. Who cared to obey the order not to visit the war prisoners' camp? Not to intercede on behalf of any prisoner, Ceres mimicked the order. They could chop off our heads, she muttered, as she, Fides, Tem, and Ciano filled up baskets of calamansi and pinapaya jam and the medicines brought by Pa. Summer was over; the Arvisus returned to Baguio. Adela and Maria to Pampanga, but said they would be back.

It was June. The Japanese Command allowed schools to reopen but many students including Ceres, Ruben, Fides, and Tem still relished their vacation, and did not go back yet. Pa needed more time to decide on the matter.

"Perhaps next school year," he said. "Let us see. In the meantime, we gather information, listen to our radio, find out what's going on. We — our people — are writing history. History is being written in the blackboard of our classroom. Wait for our soldiers to be back. Wait for Mario."

Dai-Toa-Kyoeiken was in full swing. "Assert yourselves as Orientals, Asia for Asians!" was the slogan. Tagalog was the language of instruction in schools and Nippongo, the Japanese language, was a required subject. There was a compulsory early morning mass calisthenics radio program for all students to follow — the radio taisho. The Japanese tried their best to bend Filipino allegiance away from the Commonwealth government in-exile. They tried to picture Quezon in a bad light. Words like these were always on the air on the government-controlled radio, "He is unlike Rizal who would rather die for his ideal than surrender it. Quezon lacks the martyr's firmness of character." But President Quezon in the States retaliated and continued to broadcast to the Philippines through the short wave. The Japanese were furious. "If Mr. Quezon does not stop conspiring with the enemy to jeopardize the welfare and happiness of the Filipinos, the Filipino people may be obliged to prosecute him for high treason . . . "

A new battle had begun for the minds and hearts of the Filipino people. A rehabilitation and indoctrination program was devised for the Filipino soldiers before discharge. But most of those young men joined the guerrilla movement, which operated on the surface or underground. Armed guerrilla resistance made direct contact with MacArthur's headquarters. When General Homma of the Japanese learned of this, he said, "There are still Filipinos who cannot rid themselves of their pro-American sympathies — they will be annihilated without mercy. Should Filipinos still fight for the sake of the sovereignty of the United States and American imperialism?"

Another source of belligerency came from the Huks. Although the Huks accused the USAFFE guerrillas of doing little in fighting the Japanese, and the USAFFE, on the other hand, resented encroachment of the Huks into their territory, they were both against the Japanese. The peasants were organized into a United Front Movement, the UFM, which followed Marxist-Leninist teachings of the Soviet Union. They didn't quite understand "dialectical materialism" but they understood why they were poor, not receiving enough for their labor from the landlords who were rich and were taking advantage of them. The landlords and the rich were friendly with the Japanese invaders doing business with them. Thus, the poor peasants were against the Japanese too. The Japanese had commandeered machinery, gold bullions, food, the best houses and hotels, Cadillac and Packard automobiles, and country clubs. Thus, some middle-class and rich people were resentful of the Japanese too. At the same time the Japanese were establishing organs and agencies to render service to the Filipino people. With the collaboration of Filipino officials like Benigno Aquino, Jose Laurel, Jorge Vargas, Manuel Roxas, they organized the KALIBAPI, *Kapisanan sa Paglilingkod sa Bagong Pilipinas* (Association for Service in the New Philippines).

As usual, Pa often discussed these matters with the family at dinner table, or any time they were gathered together, analyzing news reports in the papers and over the radio.

"The Japs are winning their battles militarily all over Southeast Asia and in China. But here, with us, look what happened in Bataan, in Capas, everywhere, their intentions not followed by practice. And with so many armed and unarmed elements against them, I bet they can never win over the Filipinos completely, body, mind, and soul. Not us, anyway. Time is sure running out on them," said Pa.

It was not over three months since Ma's trip to Capas but it seemed like years had gone by, having to wait for news of releases from the camp.

At last, there was an unconfirmed report that Mario would be among those to be released soon because he was suffering from beriberi and malaria. The discharge point would be at the Old Bilibid Prisons in Manila.

The whole family waited at the entrance gate as early as the first crow of the cock that morning. Mario was the first one out and Ma rushed to embrace him, followed by Pa, Ruben, Ceres, Fides, and Tem. Ma shed tears of joy.

"O - O - why the tears?" joked Pa.

"I can't believe it, I can't believe it!" sobbed Ma.

Mario had a somewhat swollen body and face, but Pa said he would take care of that. "It's not too bad."

They piled into a rented *do-kar* before words spilled out of the stories Mario had to tell of his ordeal.

"Where's our car?" asked Mario. It was the first thing he noticed missing. "And Ciano?"

"It's been grounded — no gas. Ciano too," Pa explained. Then Pa warned Ma not to feed Mario a full meal all at once, just warm soup, a gulp at a time.

"Like he was my baby again." Ma laughed.

When they reached home, Rev. Alabado was waiting for them. He too had joy written all over his wrinkled face.

"Well, well, well," greeted Pa. "Looks like you have some good news. Have you seen your son?"

"No, not yet," he answered. "But look what was delivered to me." And he pulled out of his pocket a crumpled scrap of paper on which was scrawled his son's message to him and his mother,

"Tatang, Ima. I'm fine. Returning from Bataan to Capas where the Japs conscripted me as a driver. Will be released soon. Did you get my first note? Corban."

"So that was why he was missing," said Ceres. "How did you get that note?"

"Corban threw it to the crowd and luckily, the one who caught it was somebody who knew Corban and me. So he sought me out, bless his soul, and what's more, told me more."

"More what?" asked Ceres.

"About Corban," said Rev. Alabado. "Said he was investigated by the Japanese and almost executed because he had rammed the truck he was driving into sharp bamboo clumps by the roadside and killed the Japanese he was driving for. Loss of brakes, defective steering wheel, no windshield, after all the truck was a battered one. Abandoned by the USAFFE, you know, and being collected by the Japs. Those were Corban's excuses, but at first they didn't believe him. The full story was that this Japanese had ordered Corban to go full speed on a downhill drive into a bridge, below which was a deep river they could fall into and drown. Corban argued that they had no brakes, so he wouldn't do it. But the Jap insisted, pointed a gun at him. Corban had to obey, but just before reaching the bridge he swerved and ditched the truck into bamboo clumps where broken stalks, you know the *timbo*, are sharp as swords, pierced the officer's heart killing him instantly. Corban jumped out and was unharmed except for some bruises. The man who told me this said he talked with an eyewitness in Bataan who knows what really happened. "

"Wow!" was all Ceres could say.

"Poor Nip! He didn't know how clever Filipinos are! Ha, ha, ha!" Ruben laughed.

Death of a Dream

Not long after Corban was discharged from camp and he had regained his health, he came to Manila and Pasay to visit with Ceres and her family.

"Say, you don't look like a POW, ha!" said Ceres. "Haggard and emaciated." She made a long narrow face. "Did you get to taste my pinapaya jam I sent through your father?"

"Yeah, ah no, my father told me about that. Don't you feel heroic about that, hah, like Tandang Sora? Feeding the sick and maimed captives of the war?" Corban smiled. Then seriously, he continued. "But I wasn't there. I was back in Bataan, with the Japs . . . "

"With the Japs?"

"Yes, you know, forced, conscripted as a driver. One day a Jap officer called for drivers, mechanics and skilled workers. No one of us knew what that meant. Our Filipino CO told us if we didn't obey, our barracks, the whole camp would be punished. Why jeopardize a greater number of our comrades, he said.

"I had survived the fighting, I was determined to survive till the end of the war, to see you again."

"Not as a traitor, Corban."

"No, of course not. Oh, c'mon, Ceres, you don't understand. As a captive, I would crawl for food and water, to survive. For any little favors, even for beer and cigarettes, a mosquito net. That's what war makes of captives."

Ceres was shaking her head.

"Don't shake your head. Don't you understand? We have to survive, to revenge! Back in Bataan when I realized what we were told to do for the Japs — collect derelicts, y'know, our abandoned trucks and things like that, for them — something hit me. I said to myself, no way would I help them short of their shooting me.

"I hatched a plan. And my comrades agreed with me. We would pretend to be working, stall, delay our job — that's what we did. Our contribution to the Emperor's war . . . "

"Suppose they discovered -"

"That's the risk — but as somebody said, we are great actors. Yes, we managed to fool 'em. And you know what, Ceres? Let me tell you this." Corban's eyes were shining.

"In captivity, more than in battle, I made a deeper commitment to my country and the cause for which I was fighting. Remember what we talked about in U.P. — the democratic and nationalist ideals of America and our country? I hugged those very dearly knowing you will agree with me."

Ceres smiled.

"And vowed to commit myself even unto death, to them. Not to an Emperor, his Imperial Forces and militarist government!"

"Bravo!" hailed Ceres, clapping her hands. "But really, I just prayed you'd come back safe and whole."

"And I did! Here I am." He folded his arms around her and kissed her.

For the first time Ceres felt the reality of love pouring out of her heart for a man she thought was already a casualty of the war.

"Hey, are you back in U.P.?" Corban asked, snapping her out of her thoughts.

"No, I don't think I'll go back yet even when it's allowed to open. Everything's so uncertain, Pa said."

"Yeah, as if we're in limbo — suspended living. We cannot even dream of a dream."

Later in the evening, Corban finally met Mario, and the two had so many stories to share with each other — from funny, ridiculous incidents they recalled as they hiccoughed and yelped with laughter over beer, to the most harrowing and dreadful experiences they each lived through.

Like Mario's first encounter with the Japanese enemy in Bataan. He was on patrol all agog — rifle, drawn bayonet and pistol, ready for the kill — when he suddenly came face to face with a Japanese foot soldier, just like him in full battle gear. They stared at each other eyeball to eyeball, a full ten seconds before they both realized what each was confronted with, and quick as lightning, turned about face, flashed away in opposite directions.

"Ha, ha, ha! Was I scared to death!" Mario laughed. "I was trained for artillery, not as a foot soldier. How the hell would I know how to stick that damn bayonet into which part of him, hah?"

"Me," countered Corban, "do you know I became rich overnight there? No kidding! All we did was play dice and craps. Boy, I won all the time. I taped all my winnings, some mickey mouse money, ha, ha, on my bare back, but the Jap discovered them when he ripped off the tape. Of course he confiscated them. Then my Filipino officer, he got my spoon and fork, while I had to eat with my bare fingers."

"Why did you let them?" asked Mario.

"What! Risk my life? Court martial? Bayonet?"

"Me, I won't stand for that. Money, spoon and fork, they mean power and survival, man. Times like these . . . "

"Well, I did stand up to him, this Filipino officer, the good-for-nothing captain. One day after surrender, you know, as we moved about to climb a steep hill he asked me to carry his suitcase, like I was his — what do you call that in English — his valet, yes, his suitcase so heavy and full of his clothes and things! As if I didn't have my own things to carry. So I told him: 'No, sir, I will not, you carry it yourself.' Well, he didn't shoot me, we had no more guns, ha, ha, ha!"

"There was this American," narrated Mario. "He had a canteen of water he was drinking from. I asked for a sip —'Joe,' I pleaded, 'just a sip, Joe.' He just stared at me blankly, and hugged his canteen tight to his chest. He must have kissed somebody's ass to get that canteen of water."

"Or killed him," said Corban. "Yeah, the Americans, when I was small I thought they were the greatest people on earth. They were our masters — superior in thought, words, looks, and everything. So when they made the rule in school . . . ."

"What school?" interrupted Mario.

"Angeles Elementary School in Pampanga," said Corban. "They made the rule that only English be spoken, anyone caught speaking Kapampangan would be fined one centavo. I became a spy for them. Imagine me, spying on my classmates even outside school! I used to go under their nipa houses in stilts, you know, you've seen these, and when I heard them talk in Kapampangan, I'd report them to our American principal. Only outstanding pupils were chosen for the job, you can imagine how proud I felt, being a little baluga (brown) spy for them."

"Yeah, the Americans were not all that great," said Mario. "My pa used to tell us stories about our war with them way back in 1900. Lots of stories of their cruelty too, burning barrios, killing innocent women and children, to pacify us, to give us freedom! Hah! All of them say the same things. Like the Spanish *conquistadores* and *padres* — the same! Oh my pa knows how cruel they had been too to the native Indios of the land they conquered. You know, young as he was then in 1897, he was a mail carrier of the revolutionary Katipuneros against Spain — he used to carry their letters from barrio to barrio and he would read them — so he knew why Rizal was executed. I remember Pa telling us that when he was asked what religion he had when he took the test to become a *pensionado* of America — you know, to study there — he answered Protestant, because he thought of the cruelties of the Spanish Catholic priests and friars then, from reading Rizal's novels. He reads and speaks Spanish. He's a knight of Rizal, you know. Pa is. He is always giving us history lessons from the Spanish occupation when he was a kid, to the coming of the Americans, now the Japanese. Pa and Ma, they're our history books. We should learn from history, they say, in order to have a vision. To change. Hic! Hic!"

"You and I — hic! hic! — change?" They both hiccoughed

and laughed. Then Mario added, "From tuba to beer — hic! — drinkers —" and again they hiccoughed and laughed uproariously. How they laughed!

"Say, did you get to ride those boxcars in San Fernando?" Mario asked seriously.

"Yeah, and do you know I was so relieved when I saw the railroad station because my Japanese peacetime friend, name's Takahashi, he told me we would be released there. Then, when I saw we were being shoved inside the freight cars I was glad, well, I said to myself, at least we will be riding instead of more marching."

"Yeah, me too," sighed Mario.

"Little did I know they were going to lock all the doors, it was a death trap," Corban continued. "It was an oven inside. And we were packed so tight, some men were not even standing on the floor but were held up by comrades. Every one was screaming, some at the back had passed out, with no place to fall."

"My God!" exclaimed Mario. "You're right. In mine, people were going crazy, vomiting, urinating, defecating — where else? Wow! The smell! Hell!"

"But me, I stood right next to where the sliding doors were not closed so air-tight, I put my nose into that heaven-made slit, like this" and Corban put his nose between his two fingers, "where I could get a whiff of fresh air."

"Why, I did just that too," and the two heartily congratulated each other for their great achievement. "Bad guys never die — *yerba mala nunca muere*! Ha, ha, ha!" Mario laughed. Then he added softly: "But I saw two guys, Ma's relatives. Hey, Ceres," he called, when he saw her preparing some snacks, "'who wants to go to hell with Madam Satan?' Luis! I saw him and this Jaime Noble, they were behind me, and I was going to pull them close to the slit, too, but they both fainted and I guess died. I never saw them again."

"Luis Carrascoso," said Ceres slowly. "Bless him, I shall never forget him."

"Remember Erlinda!" exclaimed Corban.

"Yeah, to boost our morale, our officer would say that, our symbol of Japanese atrocity. She was raped and buried alive with just her face above the ground," said Mario.

"Don't tell me," said Corban. "I know that. Everybody knew that. Also to boost our morale, what did they say — 'the eleven-mile convoy has left Australia' hic!"

"What about this, remember this?" asked Mario. "At O'Donnell, Capas, they said we will only be released if we can recite the pledge of allegiance to Japan and the Emperor, in Nippongo. They gave us five lines to memorize -"

"*Watakushi domowa, koko ko nippon ni kansha shimazu,*" both of them recited the first line.

"That's all I remember now, but I used to know all five lines of the pledge, so eager was I to get out of that hell," said Corban.

"Me too," said Mario. "But days and weeks passed, and we were still there. So we changed the lines: *watakushi domowa, nakayuko na, binayuneta pa!* Stooping low, and bayonetted!"

Corban recalled: "It was so sad how some could not memorize the lines, or had very poor accent, maybe they were Visayans, their tongues twisted so. But they tried their darndest best, only to succumb later to dysentery, never getting a chance to recite their piece, *maysakit na pinatay pa!* Already sick, then killed!"

They spent the whole night recalling events before, during, and after surrender. They both agreed some Japanese officers and soldiers were helpful, others, most in fact, downright cruel and arrogant. Not much different from the Spanish, American, oh yes, they added, even their own Filipino officers and men.

Ceres had nothing much to contribute to their talks; she just kept filling up their mugs of beer and platters of snacks, listened, and laughed with them.

Life began gradually to return to normal, minus the university and college schooling of the Santos Cuyugan kids. Pa was still unconvinced that the Japanese were permanently occupying the country.

In the neighborhood some mothers asked Ceres to give piano lessons to their children for a small fee. Ceres readily agreed. It was something to do which she enjoyed.

One neighbor, five-year-old Perla Labrador was a handicapped polio victim. Both her arms and legs had lost their muscle control but with constant practice and physical therapy she was soon able to play little simple pieces on the piano. Ceres considered this success her very own too. So happy was she for Perla's progress in her piano playing, she did not mind at all when Perla would love-match her to her uncle, a young Magsaysay of the Zambales Magsaysays.

"Oh, Teacher is blushing," Perla would tease. "You know, he always asks about you when he comes to visit here." And when he was around, Perla would call out from across the narrow street where she lived. "Teacher, Teacher, come give me my piano lesson. He's here, he's here!" How embarrassing, Ceres would mutter, blushing, but because Perla was such a lovable girl, Ceres would come to please her.

Her other pupils came to the house for their lessons. Ma would listen to Ceres get so emotional and cranky when the little kids made mistakes or did not play with expression.

"My, my, Ceres, those kids are so young! What do they know of suffering? How can you expect them to feel what they are playing?" Ma would say.

"But, Ma, I haven't suffered either, have I? But I can feel. I can put myself in a sufferer's body, into her mind and heart, feel her heartaches and pain." Ceres remembered Miss Marcela, her piano teacher's advice.

"Can you, really, truly?" asked Ma.

"I try, I can try," said Ceres.

One day, many months later, a perfect stranger appeared at the gate. Ciano went to see him and announced that the man came from faraway Davao in Mindanao. He had some news to relay to the family. Ma and Pa and all the children were home and they all came forward.

"I have come to tell you about Dr. John Santos Cuyugan and his family. They had all been killed — massacred — by the Japanese," he said.

"Uncle John!" exclaimed Ceres.

Pa could not believe what he heard.

"It can't be," he protested. "He is director of the Mintal Hospital

— a Japanese hospital!"

"But it's true, sir," said the stranger. "You may go there. You will find many witnesses to the killing."

After a while, Pa sobered up. "I'm sorry," he apologized. "I have not asked you in."

The stranger introduced himself as a barrio captain in the vicinity of Uncle John's farm. He narrated the ghastly details of the massacre.

"We heard that the Japanese marines were coming to our barrio. So we all evacuated our homes and fled to the hills except Dr. John Santos Cuyugan's family. The Doctor did not like to leave his home. We persuaded him to leave but he said he was safe there. The Japanese would not touch him because he was their doctor.

"But he was wrong. When they came, they herded the whole family — the whole household including nieces and maids living with them — to a field at the back of their house. And there," the man could not continue. He wiped his face.

"I had not left my yard. A few other men were also still packing their belongings. I was hidden by a cluster of banana trees, about twelve meters away. I saw everything," he continued. "Doctor John, he was pleading to the Japanese to spare the girls, he had eight daughters in all, you know, and his wife, Pilaring, and all the rest. Me, kill me, he offered, don't kill them, he pleaded, I offer myself.

"But it was no use. The Japanese first raped the girls and his wife. Then with their sabers hacked them all to death. By then Doctor John had cracked, gone crazy, screaming out loud with all his might, so heart-wrenching a scream, the people in the hills heard it, before he, last of all, was slashed with sweeping strokes to death."

Pa could not speak for a very long time. For the first time, Ceres saw Pa's face in deep shadows.

"Maybe they discovered he was an American citizen," Pa said slowly, softly, as if to himself.

"What!" exclaimed Ma. She did not know that. No one but Pa knew that Uncle John had taken up citizenship in the States, but instead of staying there, he preferred to return to his native land.

The barrio captain excused himself and as suddenly as he had appeared, he was gone, leaving the Santos Cuyugan family to their unspeakable sorrow.

With the loss of his brother, Pa grieved the end of his dream, their dream, of a cancer research program. They had started to lay the foundation: the basic research would be under the University of the Philippines; then they would set up the clinical research and a small hospital, the Santos Cuyugan Clinic. But the war had interrupted their plans, and now this.

What was there left of their lifelong dream?

Cockroaches, Cheer Up!
(Battle of Manila)

*T*he months and years rolled by — a kaleidoscope of horror and hope, loyalty and treachery, nightmare and dream, war and peace.

The family's short wave radio continued to supply the news and commentaries not available in the local papers and radio taisho of the Japanese. It had become the family's heartbeat to the outside world and the underground.

They learned that the war in Europe and in Asia had turned around. The winners had become the losers; the killers, killed. Winston Churchill of England had said: "When Hitler is finished, we shall lay the cities of Japan in ashes." Italy had surrendered unconditionally. General Eisenhower of the United States had begun his assault on Hitler's Fortress Europe. General Douglas MacArthur had begun his "up the ladder island-hopping" toward Japan with terrific naval and aerial bombardments. When Roosevelt asked him: "Douglas, where do we go from here?" His reply was: "Leyte, Mr. President, and then Luzon." The Big Three — Churchill, Roosevelt, and Stalin — held a conference in which they agreed that the post-war world should be ordered by "Four Policemen" — the United States, Britain, Russia, and China.

"Hey, how about us?" Ruben asked, interrupting the news. "Don't we have a say?"

"Stupid!" said Mario. "We don't count. We're not even cockroaches."

The news in the Philippines was that a Preparatory Commission for Philippine Independence was created to prepare the granting of independence to the Philippines by Japan, ahead of the American promise at the end of the Commonwealth in 1946.

"Hah! America and Japan, they're racing to give us independence, who'll win?" mocked Ceres. "But first stop killing us, please, on bended knees."

The newscast continued, "In the new Constitution, Japan would be the protector and consultant of all agencies of the government. Jose Laurel was elected president. He had left for Tokyo accompanied by Benigno Aquino and Jorge Vargas. There he was asked to declare war with the United States. Laurel was shocked, he said he was not prepared and did not expect this! He could not comply. But upon constant pressure he acceded to all the Japanese demands: retention of all military facilities for the military activities of the Japanese forces, to safeguard each other's territorial integrity and the independence of the Philippines; retention of media control and of government corporations; political, economic, and military control for the successful prosecution of the war of Greater East Asia. Laurel was made Supreme Adviser of the MAKAPILI — *Kalipunang Makabayan ng mga Pilipino* (Patriotic League of Filipinos) — whose members are reputed to be informers and potential spies, armed by the Japanese and trusted more than the Philippine Constabulary. But the majority of the Filipino people see them as traitors and fear them as much as the Japanese."

"Some of them are Kapampangan," said Pa.

"Hala, maybe they are your relatives, Pa," Mario said.

Finally, Laurel declared a state of emergency and martial law all over the land.

"Laurel is urging Filipinos to fight on the side of Japan,"

said Pa. "While the guerrillas, the Huks, the UFM, other left wing opposition groups like the Peasant Union, many labor organizations, they are said to be now controlling many towns and provinces, are calling on us to fight the Japanese invaders."

"Yehey-y-y-y! I'm for Japan!" shouted Mario.

"I'm for America!" said Fides.

"I'm Filipino, so I'm for Filipinas!" said Ruben.

Ceres was silent. Was there any question for whom they were, she asked herself. Only the leaders in government were pulling them this way and that, so that the people were confused.

The broadcaster asked over the radio, "Which is their true government? Once again, the Filipinos are in a quandary."

Not us, thought Ceres, not those who stand strong as a rock. Not those who keep in their hearts the spirit of Mactan, Pinaglabanan, Samar, the dungeons of Fort Santiago. From north to south, they are fighting in the hills and towns, they whose faith never waver in the land of their ancestors. This was what Pa and Ma had always taught her and her family in their history lessons.

Then Pa said, "If only Laurel had divorced his government entirely from Japanese control, he might have gained the people's support." On second thought he added: "But how is that possible under the circumstances, if one has to retain one's job, not to speak of saving one's neck?"

The family continued listening to the news: "President Quezon died in the United States and is succeeded by Vice-President Sergio Osmena. General Tomoyuki Yamashita, the Tiger of Malaya, replaced General Kuroda Shigenori in Manila. A powerful American armada has entered Leyte Gulf and landed a massive invasion force on Leyte. General MacArthur with Osmena, waded ashore, and MacArthur announced: 'People of the Philippines, I have returned.' "

Months later, one night in the pitch darkness and deadly silence before dawn, Ciano knocked at the door of Ceres' bedroom and woke her up.

"Ma'am, there's a young man at the gate to see you," Ciano whispered.

"Me? Corban?" asked Ceres.

"No, Ma'am. I know Mr. Corban and Rev. Alabado. Not they. Said it's important. He did not give his name. I saw something bulging inside his shirt—maybe a gun. Maybe, Ma'am, he's a g . . ."

"Shhhh," Ceres put her finger to his lips. "What time is it, Ciano?" She asked, as she fumbled for her slippers and wrapped a robe over her pajamas.

"I don't know, but soon the cock will crow," said Ciano.

"Don't turn on the lights," said Ceres, as she inched her way to the porch and stopped just before descending the stairs. She peered into the dark and saw the dark silhouette of a man she could not recognize.

"Who is it?" Ceres asked him.

"Ceres, please let me in. Trust me," the man said.

Ceres vaguely recognized the voice but could not place it. She hesitated a second before she told Ciano to open the gate and let him in.

"You're," Ceres began after she turned on a dim light in the porch and saw his face.

"Porch lizard," he said.

"You're still a porch lizard." Ceres smiled. "But in my porch this time. Come in, have some coffee."

"Listen," said porch lizard. "I'm," he stopped. They were talking in whispers, but he noticed Ciano watching them.

"Oh, he's okay, he's our driver. He hates the Japs too, he was slapped by them," said Ceres.

"I haven't much time, put me up here for just a couple of hours to rest. In the morning I shall push on to Intramuros — there are many of us but there as many Japs too — that's where they're making their last stand. If we don't get 'em, they will kill more civilians. Don't go walking out in the streets. There'll be terrible street fighting," the man warned Ceres. "If you have short wave radio, listen by the hour. This is the crucial moment. But be very careful."

Ceres nodded. "Here, here, on this couch," she pointed out where he could rest.

Porch Lizard took a sip from the cup of coffee Ciano handed to him and lay down on the couch. Ceres wanted to ask him some more questions, but he was already snoring, curled up hugging his shirt like a baby.

Ceres tiptoed back to her bedroom. When she awoke in the morning, the man was gone.

The drive toward Manila had begun. The radio broadcast announced, "MacArthur had planned a grand victory parade with himself in the lead, closing in on the city and ringing it. But up to now MacArthur himself has not announced it. Meanwhile we have learned that General Yamashita moved his command and withdrew to the mountains up north. But many of his troops are stranded in Manila, and against his orders to abandon Manila, the naval airforce, mostly kamikaze suicide pilots have opted to remain in Manila and fight to the last. So stay home. Stay home! Laurel, too, was flown to Baguio. For the second time, Manila is declared an open city.

"American forces with Filipino guerrillas have now surfaced from underground and they have approached the city from the north and south. You hear naval bombardments from the Bay and aerial bombardments from the sky — signal to the people that the time has come at last for the final push to victory and peace. This is a warning again, for you to stay home!"

Shortly afterwards, Ceres played the piano and Fides began to sing. First her vocal exercises, then some songs.

Just then a man passing through Sandejas street stopped in front of the Santos Cuyugan house. He shook the gate lightly but it made a noisy clanking sound. Then he called in very clear English, "May I come in? Just short while?"

Ceres and Fides stopped and peeped out to the gate. Japanese, a Japanese soldier in full uniform! The short wave radio was the first thing that Ceres thought of! She felt cold all over.

"I just want to hear music. I love music too," Ceres heard him say. Well, she thought, if he loved music and could speak English, he could not be very bad, he would not do much harm. So she called Ciano and whispered to him, "Quick, cover the radio with a blanket, lock the door of the room. Then let that Jap in."

"*Arigato, arigato go sai masta*, thank you, thank you very much," the Japanese said, bowing and bowing to Ceres and Fides. "My name is Oscar."

"That's not a Japanese name," said Ceres.

"I'm a Christian," he said.

"Not a Buddhist? You speak good English," said Ceres.

"Yes, I study English, and I can sing too," Oscar said. Then he approached the piano and played a few notes.

"What do you want to sing?" Fides asked.

"Oh Susannah! You know that?" Oscar asked.

Ceres played the piano while Fides and Oscar sang Oh Susannah!, then Auld Lang Syne, Swanee River, and many other English songs.

Pa and Ma were in the bedroom, listening. When Ma heard the song, "Beautiful Dreamer," she whispered to Pa, "My favorite," and she sang softly too.

Then Oscar requested Ceres to play "God Bless America."

So Ceres played and they all sang:

God bless America, land that I love
Stand beside her and guide her
through the night
with the light from above.
From the mountains, to the prairies
to the oceans white with foam,
God bless America
* my home sweet home . . . my home sweet home.*

"You like American songs?" asked Ceres.

"I don't like this war. I pray it will end soon," he said. "Japan make mistake making war, invading your country. I'm so sorry," he added.

Then they heard the booming outside.

"I suggest you put basins, you know, porcelain basins, over your head — like this," and he cupped his hands over his head, "good protection against shrapnel, you know shrapnel?"

"Oh, like helmets." Fides laughed. "*Arigato*," she added.

Fides and Oscar enjoyed singing together while Ceres

accompanied them on the piano. They sang and talked far into the night. Pa and Ma and the rest of the family let them. It was better, they said, than if he'd go poking around the house.

Before he left, he tied some leaves atop his cap. "I'm going to the mountains, to die there."

The next day, Pa came home from the hospital with something in his mind to do, fast and with utmost urgency. Without having greeted Ma, he went straight into the small room where the short wave radio lay on the desk and grabbed it with his two hands, with the blanket Ciano had wrapped it with the night before.

"Quick, Mario, Ruben, come with me to the backyard," he whispered.

"Why Pa, why?" asked Mario.

"Just come, no questions," Pa said.

The three rushed down the back stairs, past the garage, past the mango tree, to the thick clumps of banana trees crowding each other by the high concrete wall where their garden ended.

"We have to bury this radio into the ground here." Then Pa realized he had forgotten to bring a spade, a hoe, or anything, to dig with. "Run back to the garage, Mario, get a pick, a shovel, any . . ." Mario was off before Pa could say what he wanted.

In a flash, Mario was back with Pa's garden tools, and they began digging while Pa explained in whispers why they had to do this.

"Some Japanese officials are coming to our house, I was told," Pa began.

"Who told you?" asked Ruben.

"At the hospital, never mind who. So many people have been picked up and brought to Fort Santiago, tortured and killed, for listening to short wave," Pa wiped his sweating brow with his hand.

"Yes, I know, like the guerrillas," interrupted Mario.

"Even women like Josefa Llanes Escoda, I heard she was so brave," said Pa. Then he added, "Don't tell Ma just yet, she'll get nervous."

"Pa, you're the one that's nervous. Look, your hands are shaking. How can you operate tomorrow?" asked Ruben.

"Yeah, Pa, your hands are not steady," said Mario.

"You silly boys, I'll get over this. Tomorrow I'll be as cool and calm as a dead rat." Pa smiled.

They dug a hole two feet deep, three feet wide, kissed the radio wrapped in a blanket with a "thank you, you have served us well," lovingly laid it on a thick adobe stone, and then covered it with earth and stones and weeds.

"Whew!" Pa breathed a deep sigh of relief. "Now let's walk back to the house as if we just did a bit of gardening here. Not a word to anybody, remember, not even to Ma and the girls."

"But they'll ask, they'll miss the radio," said Mario.

"No, they won't notice, with those Japs if they come here. Okay, if they ask, just whisper to them," said Pa.

"See, Pa, you're nervous, you can't think well," said Ruben.

Sure enough, the next day a couple of Japanese officers occupied the Santos Cuyugan bungalow. They did not send the family away. Ma and Pa gave them their own room. One of the officers was a young man and he took a fancy to Fides. Fides skillfully kept him at bay by singing endlessly to him while Ceres accompanied her on the piano, Ruben on the violin.

After two days, Ceres was getting panicky having to live with them. On the third day she thought of an ingenious way to end their stay and get them out of the house. She told Pa her plan and Pa agreed. "You're a genius," he said. Ceres began to cough and cough without let-up. The whole day, all through the night she coughed. She could no longer play the piano.

Pa told the Japanese that she was suffering from a terminal case of tuberculosis. "Maybe she got tired," he said. "Like Quezon, very infectious disease."

The trick worked. After saying they were sorry for her, they packed up, ready to leave. But not before two or more Japanese soldiers dropped by as if on cue, lugging cans of gasoline which they poured all over the house and ignited. The family, Pa and Ma and the children and household help, all together, rushed out of the house, thankful they were not locked in. They watched in the yard, shivering in helpless abandon as the house and the car in the garage were devoured by the flames so fast, they could not save any of their furniture and things, all turned to smoldering ashes. The Japanese shouted as they marched off: "*Banzai! Banzai!* We fight, not retreat and surrender! More Japanese here in Manila to kill and die!"

After the fire had died down to gray smoke, Ma took stock. "At least we are alive! That's the best thing," she said. "Only two items were saved from the fire." She revealed the secret she had been keeping all these years in preparation she said, for a time they might be forced to run to the hills — wrapped in a silk bandanna cloth and pinned to her chemise were her jewelries. She was never without them. "Even when I take a bath," she joked. As for the second item, Ma had stashed away inside a big duffel bag that Indang Manda Abad Santos had given her, also secretly, tons and tons of mickey mouse money, the money printed by the Japanese, which could buy very little of already scarce food, "but better than nothing at all," she said. The duffel bag was sandwiched among the sandbags that didn't burn.

"No, Ma," said Mario, "there's another thing." Mario and Ruben brought forth the radio they now retrieved from under the ground where they had buried it. Then they told the story to Ma and the girls.

Ceres had the deepest thought about it.

"*So desuka,*" she said, almost to herself, "those Japs were indeed suspicious we had short wave radio here, always peeping into our rooms, waiting for our tongue to slip and say something to reveal it. But God taught us not to make it happen, right, Pa?"

More and more Japanese soldiers were marching up and down Sandejas street, in front of their burnt-out house. The family quickly reassembled their dug-out with the unburned sandbags, and invited the neighbors who had no such shelters in their homes to come into theirs. The dug-out was packed full of the old and young — men, women, and children. When they heard heavy boots marching on the street, they covered the mouths of the children who might cough or cry and give away their hiding place to the retreating Japanese soldiers. How many times did they all hold their breaths, their hearts thumping fast when they heard those heavy-booted soldiers shaking the iron-grilled gate until it jangled mightily, to break it open and force themselves in, shouting *Kura! Kura!* The women prayed a hundred rosaries to a hundred saints imploring their divine aid to save them from the fires of those traitorous devils. The men stood guard at the entrance to the dug-out ready to defend themselves and their kin with iron bars, shovels, axes, anything, even Pa's garden hose, to do battle with the enemy who dared climb over or force open the locked gate. They could hear the booming outside now and then. "*Dios ko!*" somebody cried. "What's going to happen to us? Whose guns are those?" Another one answered, "American naval and aerial bombardments. Americans bombarding us, Japanese bayonetting us."

Then there were intervals of silence. The men, women, children, and infants were dead still, no one said a word, or cried, or laughed.

As they waited and waited, and heard no marching sounds outside, nothing happened, Mario got restless. He tried to convince Pa to let him out, venture into the street. "Maybe they're gone. I'll see," he said.

"No," said Pa. "Stay put."

"Pa, I'm not a baby, 'member I was in Bataan," said Mario.

Pa turned his back. And Mario slipped out quietly, climbed over the gate, and jumped into the street. First he looked around. Then he walked as fast as he could, sticking close to the bushes fronting the street so that he could quickly seek cover should he hear the heavy boots, until he reached the corner of Vito Cruz and Sandejas. He saw a billowing black smoke swelling and rising up, turning into reddish blue. Then he saw women, mothers hugging their infants in their arms fleeing their burning homes. Suddenly, some fully-camouflaged Japanese soldiers came out of nowhere, caught these mothers, grabbed their babies, tossed them up into the air like basketballs, and on the way down, speared them in their glittering sharp bayonets. The soldiers were too preoccupied with their beastly game, they didn't see Mario crouching behind an empty parked car nearby. One soldier with a devilish glint in his eyes looked so deliriously delighted with what he was doing, he laughed and laughed, while another played catch-balls with the babies. "For our Emperor! For our Emperor!" Mario thought he heard them shout with such glee.

Shaking with horror, Mario dashed away, unmindful of the danger of being seen by the Japanese. He couldn't bear to see what would happen to the mothers prostrate on the ground, helpless, screaming and wailing, begging for their babies. The nerves in his senses directed his brain to do something. His hands itched for a knife, a bayonet, guns — where were the guerrillas, where was God? His mouth salivated, and his spit arched in the air now grayish with ash. He heard the crackle of fire spreading to the neighborhood. His nose twitched with the thought of the fresh young blood of the babies — ohhhhhh, the babies! His brain whirled an uproar.

Then he saw some men rushing out of their homes. "Hoy, hoy," he called to them hysterically, "you know what they're doing over there? You know what they're doing to the babies?"

The men stared at him blankly. Mario told them in broken pieces of words he could hardly utter. "They im-im-impaled the ba-bies in their ba-bayonets!"

"*Bahala na ang Diyos* (Leave that to God's mercy)," one of the men said. Then he added: "Many families left their homes, sought refuge in the Catholic schools like St. Scho and De La Salle over there. They thought these devils would respect the place, but they were mistaken, *naku*, they were massacred there too. Some pregnant women, like that Cojuangco lady, know her? Another one, Asela Carlos . . . "

"Oh no! not them!" was all Mario could say.

"Well," continued the man, "they pleaded to their captors to spare them, but they were bayonetted as they were praying on their knees in the chapel. And many religious Brothers of La Salle, mercilessly murdered too . . . "

"I know them, oh my God!" said Mario.

"That's why we say what can we do? Our fate is in God's hands, but you better take care, man," the man said finally.

Mario sprinted on but as he looked back he caught a glimpse of the man he had just talked with running away from the fire that had now engulfed the whole neighborhood, as the houses he had passed along Sandejas street suddenly burst into flames, and more people were coming out into the street, running here and there. Flames and smoke filled the air. Mario, blinded by the smoke, groped his way back. He missed the gate, ran past it. He was in a daze. Retracing his steps, he found the gate, climbed over it, and slipped into the dug-out. For a full minute, he was speechless. But Ma could not wait. "What did you do, what happened, Mario? What? What?" she asked frantically.

Mario relayed the harrowing scenes he had witnessed and the stories he had been told, to eager ears awaiting him.

Pandemonium broke loose. Many of the neighbors got up from sleep and rest, ready to rush out to see if their houses were burning, see what they could save from them.

"Wait, wait, wait!" shouted Pa. "It's not safe yet. You heard what Mario saw!" And he and Mario barred them at the entrance with their bodies and arms outstretched.

The women screamed and wailed, the babies and children cried and fretted.

"Shhhh!" shushed Ma. "Our house burned, too, but we have to save our lives."

"They have gone berserk, desperate! *Puñeta! Leche!*" Pa cussed and spat out Spanish words in his extreme anger, and the redness of rage flooded his face.

"Oh God of mercy!" whispered Ma. "At least one of Herod's soldiers spared the Baby Jesus."

It was then Ceres divulged her secret to the family huddled in a semi-circle, "You know, a guerrilla partisano had come here quietly in the night and told me he and many comrades were rushing to Intramuros where the Japs were making their last stand."

"But why didn't they deploy here — here — all around — too?" interrupted Mario. "If I only have guns."

Just then they heard an urgent call from the gate.

"Doctol, Doctol, come, emergency. It's Misteh Tan, Misteh Tan," called a voice.

Pa peeped out to see who was calling him. It was the Chinese owner of the small sari-sari retail store across the street.

"Quick, Doctol, my helper-boy, he's been bayonetted, please come," implored Mr. Tan.

Before Pa rushed out, he warned everybody, "Keep quiet, don't peep out, don't go out!"

Pa could hardly find his way as he staggered out, so thick and black was the smoke enveloping the whole neighborhood. "Oh my God!" He choked and coughed. He felt so helpless. But as a surgeon, he didn't feel that helpless to save the life of Mr. Tan's houseboy. So he hurried on.

He found Mr. Tan's helper lying on a bench bleeding to death. His abdomen had been slashed, his intestines and stomach sticking out of his body. In a lightning flash, Pa scrubbed his hands and arms with plain soap and water, gathered the entrails and stitched them all back in with an improvised thread and needle Mr. Tan sold in his store. "Good, your store has not been burned," said Pa.

Mr. Tan nodded. "I have plenty water, I wet all around," he said.

Then Pa sprinkled sulfathiazole powder he had crushed between his fingers, all over the wound. "I always have this handy in my pocket, it's my treasure," he told Mr. Tan, smiling. "Here," and he handed Mr. Tan sulfa tablets, "give him two to drink right away, that's to prevent infection."

Mr. Tan thanked Pa profusely. "*Salamat*, thank you, Doctol, you always ready, hah? *Laging handa*, Doctol, *talaga!*" Then he told Pa that his helper just happened to look through a small opening in the store and was seen by a Japanese soldier passing by who yanked him out and without saying a word stuck his bayonet into the boy's stomach, swung it left to right, almost cutting his body in half.

"Doctol," said Mr. Tan in whispers, "I heard news that street fighting is still going on in Walled City, you know, Intramuros, in Manila. Many Japanese snipers and stragglers making their last stand there, from street to street, house to house, room to room. Tens of thousands of people killed, many more dying. But it's already mopping-up operations. War here ending, Doctol. Good news, hah, Doctol?"

"Good news? With so many dying?" asked Pa. "Keep yourselves locked up inside, it's not over yet," Pa warned Mr. Tan.

As Pa was about to rush back across the street into the dug-out, Mr. Tan held his arm, "Wait, take this, for your people very many there," and he handed Pa a big can of crackers.

Back in the dug-out, Pa told Ma Mr. Tan's news on the fighting. "Oh God, it's terrible," Ma said. She faced the crowd and spoke out loud.

"May I have your attention, please," she began, but she had to repeat it three times before the excited chatter died down. "We must pray, Lord, protect us," Ma could not go on for it seemed to her, their only protection was silence and obedience. So she ended with " . . . Thy Will be done."

"The war is coming to an end, but so is our city," Pa said mournfully.

"No, Pa," said Ma. "We will survive. Cheer up!"

"Yeah, yeah," said Ruben. "Cockroaches, cheer up!"

"Monkeys," said Fides. And she sang softly,

"Oh the monkeys have no tails in Zamboanga,
They've been bitten by the whales, la, la, la . . ."

"Shhhh!" Ma stopped her.

"Monkeys, savages, cockroaches, cheer up!" said Ruben.

A few days later, Pa thought it was already safe to leave the shelter. For all of a day and night, they had not heard a single marching boot go up or down Sandejas street. One by one, the men, women, and children and the Santos Cuyugan family who had lived in the shelter for days with just water to drink and some biscuits to eat, stretched legs and arms and wiggled out like earthworms from underground.

But where to go?

A most tragic sight greeted them as they emerged outside. Manila and Pasay were levelled to the ground. Some concrete walls of residential buildings stood, still smoldering; other houses had collapsed completely into piles of charred wood and ashes. A jungle of pockmarked concrete buildings with protruding, bent, and twisted steel bars and pipes and wires, slithering like snakes curving here and there, stood upright like skeletons and worms on a desert land of crumpled rubble and tin. People bending low in anguish, in endless procession burying their dead.

Hope Springs Eternal

$\mathcal{I}$n the Santos Cuyugan's wide open yard, the cockroaches and earthworms crawled back into the dug-out, or pitched camp. They made tents out of blankets or bedsheets or coverlets as roof cover tied to poles they salvaged from the rubble, to put their things under in case it rained. They had nowhere to live while going about the tedious task of collecting serviceable two- and four-inch nails and partially burned pieces of lumber for the makeshift temporary *barung-barong* shacks in their own home lots until the lumber yards and hardwares reopened in the city. Just something — even a battered galvanized tin roof — over their heads, and patched up burned timber to enclose them in their sleep and dreams.

The Santos Cuyugan family worked quickly, too, to build their *barung-barong* shack with the charred pieces of their house. Corban had become a porch lizard of the family. He drove a truck of the American Army and brought some pieces of lumber, a can of powdered eggs, and chocolates, to win piece by piece not only the heart of Ceres but of the rest of the family and the neighbors who were homeless and needed help to rehabilitate themselves. Sometimes Ceres thought it was just to show off that he was back in the Army, the U. S. Army.

"You can't win me with U. S. goods, and attitude," Ceres joked.

"But I'm not bragging — you waited for this for four years, didn't you?" Corban countered.

"For GI Corban, not GI Joe!" said Ceres.

Pa and Ma often visited with each of the families in rows upon rows of *barung-barong* lining Sandejas street.

"How about you, Doctor, how are you doing?" a neighbor asked in turn.

"Oh, can't you see our mansion?" Pa asked.

"Really? You're joking, Doctor," said another neighbor.

"Yes, really, it's magic. Sometimes it's there, then it's gone," said Pa. "Like a dream. "

"But this is a nightmare," said Ma. "I lost my piano."

"Yes, yes," the neighbors who were listening all agreed. "An endless nightmare."

Not long afterwards, electricity was restored and the family installed temporary electric wiring in their shack so they could plug in their radio, most important of all. Newspapers had not come out and once again the radio was their window to the world. They heard the news that MacArthur brought Osmena to Malacanang Palace and promptly installed him as head of the Philippine government, while Tokyo ordered Laurel flown to Japan, to establish there a Japanese sponsored government-in-exile. With Laurel were Aquino, Osias, Capinpin. Those left behind in Baguio soon joined or escaped toward the American forces — Quintin Paredes, Teofilo Sison, Manuel Roxas, Jose Yulo, Antonio de las Alas, Pedro Sabido, Jose Paez, Jose Sanvictores, Claro Recto, Rafael Alunan, Emilio Abello.

"Do you know all these people, Pa?" asked Ceres.

"Some, yes. But I'm keeping track of 'em — so I'll remember who are the traitors, the collaborators, the patriots . . . "

"But they were only trying to save their lives, Pa," said Ceres.

"Exactly, only their lives, only their well-being, only their pockets. Listen," said Pa, as the broadcaster continued with the newscast. "The United States has turned its guns and planes toward Japan. Roosevelt has died and Harry Truman succeeded him as

President of the United States. Over in Europe, the news is that Mussolini was shot by partisans. Hitler had shot himself too. Germany has surrendered to the Allies, and V-E is now celebrated throughout the United States. Russia has finally declared war on Japan and invaded Korea."

Then on August 4, 1945, an excited announcement flashed over the radio: "A super-fortress 'Enola Gay' dropped the first atom bomb on the city of Hiroshima in Japan. Over half of the city was wiped out. It is estimated that over a hundred thousand people were instantly killed, and many more are expected to die from radiation."

"What's the atom bomb, never heard," asked Ruben.

"The newest invention of death — the most destructive," said Pa. "What kind of people are we, what kind of a world are we living in?"

"But Pa, you are a doctor, not a philosopher," said Ceres.

"Yes, I cannot understand all this," he said.

Then they heard that a second atom bomb was dropped on Nagasaki when the Japanese command stubbornly held on. "But the Japanese realized," the newscaster announced, "that the United States has the superweapon that could destroy their nation, so Tokyo finally sued for peace on one condition: Emperor Hirohito remain in the Imperial throne. MacArthur will accept the surrender of Japan. World War II has ended."

"If only atoms were to be used for medicine, to save lives, instead of to destroy. Atoms for life, not for death . . . " Pa said sadly.

But no one now paid serious attention to what Pa was saying. There was total jubilation in the air. Everyone in the family was in a happy, care-free mood. Everyone was full of jokes and songs and joy. The kids especially. They wanted to do everything they had been afraid to do for four long and boring years. Run and jump and work and laugh and be careless. Be silly.

Mario, following Corban, rejoined the United States Armed Forces in the Far East (USAFFE) but none of the officers he talked to knew what to do with him. "But I was inducted into the USAFFE at the outbreak of the war," he insisted.

"Sure, I believe you, be with us, but I have no authority to put you on the payroll," said one officer. So Mario worked for a pittance as a gasoline boy in the gas depot.

Ruben joined a gang of teenagers making the rounds of charred buildings and houses that had been occupied by the Japanese forces, to loot them of anything that could be salvaged. He had a whopping good time running from skeleton house to house and coming out with armfuls of junk — fancy jewelry, clocks, pens — including partially burned furniture he dragged and pushed down the street to the yard.

Pa was furious. "Stop it, Ruben!" he cried. "You're a looter!"

"I'm just a looter of a looter," said Ruben.

"That doesn't make you any better," said Pa.

"But it's fun, Pa, fun! We'd never had fun like now. See what I got —" and he laid out half-burned books, watches, broken-down typewriter, other office equipment, that filled the top of the dining table.

No one could stop his abounding joy long suppressed by deprivation. The next day he sneaked out when Pa left for the hospital. Tem wanted to go with him but Ruben said no. "I'm going far away to a gold mine, for boys only."

He was gone all day and Ma was getting worried he might have been sniped by a Japanese still lurking around. In the afternoon, before sunset, a weapons carrier screeched to a stop right in front of the house.

"Ruben! He's been caught — ay, this boy giving us trouble," Ma mumbled as she, Ceres, Fides, and Tem raced to the gate.

There sat Ruben, a brown conqueror with a gleeful smile, perched on top of a table inside the weapons carrier. Grinning beside him was a GI Joe in uniform.

"Ma, meet my friend Kenneth, Ken. He gave me this table. It's MacArthur's desk. Intact. No damage, Ma. From Manila Hotel." Ruben pounded the desk with clenched fists.

Ma was flabbergasted. She just opened her mouth.

"Pleased to meet ya, Ma'am," said Ken.

"Where'd you come from?" at last Ma asked.

" 'm from Missouri, Ma'am," the GI said with a certain

Southern drawl.

"I mean where'd you meet my son?" she asked.

"Ma, at Manila Hotel, to look for things. The Japs occupied that too," said Ruben.

"Yoh son, he can have this, the best in town," Ken said, as he and Ruben lifted the heavy table onto their shoulders and brought it down on the pavement just before the gate. It was a beautiful desk with three drawers on each side and hand-carved all over.

Ma shed off her nervousness and introduced the girls. Then she hastily asked them to prepare food and drinks and invited this GI Joe to dinner. But Ken declined and said he'd consider Ma's invitation some other time.

"All right," said Ma. "That's a raincheck," she added, trying to be Americanized.

Not a few days later Ken took up Ma on that raincheck. He came to visit one late afternoon, and brought along two other GIs, all spick and span in their uniforms — Dave and George. Ma prepared special Filipino dishes. The city market, for months so empty, was slowly filling up with meat, fish, fruits, and vegetables. *Pancit* for long life, *lumpia* with fresh lettuce leaves and *ubod*, *adobo* of chicken and pork, *sinigang* of catfish and mustard leaves for soup, *leche flan* for dessert.

Ken, Dave, and George ate Ma's special dishes with gusto.

"Why, I'm surprised you like our food," said Ma.

"Oh yeah, yeah," said Ken, nodding and nodding. "An' yoh girls too. They're very purty," he said seriously.

Ma thought he was joking and was naughty. She was not taking any chances. So in the kitchen, she took the girls, Ceres, Fides, and Tem aside and whispered: "Don't you go flirting with those GIs, I warn you, hah! *Hanggang pier lang kayo !* (They won't take you with them to the States, only up to the pier!)"

Now, Ceres thought, she was going steady with her boy friend, Corban; Fides was too young and ambitious, she had no mind yet for boys. Tem too. So Ma need not have worried. But it was fun with those Americans.

More and more GIs came to their house with Ken and

Dave and George. Ceres invited other girls from the neighborhood and they would have a shindig at home. Ken brought some playing records and an old phonograph. They jitterbugged and boogied, they chacha cha-ed and rhumba-ed till the wee hours of the morning. They sang, "*He's in the army now, he's the boogie, woogie bugle boy from company B . . .*"

In time Ken and Dave and George said they had fallen in love with Ceres, Fides, and Tem, and one after another they each proposed marriage: Ken to Ceres, Dave to Fides, and George to Tem.

But Ceres said: "No, we're Filipinas, not Americans."

Fides said: "You'll go back to America and have girl friends, maybe wives back home."

Tem shook her head, "No, no, no, no touch!"

That was that. They boogied and chachacha-ed and rhumba -ed to their hearts' content, but no touch. Oh, it was nice and fun to flirt with these Americans, Ceres thought, but no touch. It was good, too, to have Ma's hands on the brake.

Weeks later, after dinner, the kids began assessing their worldly possessions, the history lessons they had learned, and their dreams. It was Pa's idea.

"What shall we do with all our mickey mouse money?" asked Mario, the accountant of the family. "We have so much, but this money doesn't talk," he joked.

"I know what money talks now," said Ceres. "Dollars. The Americans are back. Victory Joe, chocolates, powdered egg."

"As for me," said Fides, " a kiss from Ma made me a singer, not GI Joe, not chocolates, not powdered egg."

Everybody laughed. Then Fides sang, a capella, because there was no piano yet to accompany her:

> *You are my sunshine, my only sunshine*
> *You make me happy when skies are gray*
> *You'll never know dear how much I love you*
> *Please don't take my sunshine away.*

Just then Corban sauntered up the stairs on time to join the singing. "Second verse," he said, "everybody sing!" And he conducted the chorus as in the American camp.

"And now for our Spanish ancestors and *conquistadores*," said Fides, as she sang:

> *Vesame, vesame mucho*
> *Como se fuese esta noche es la ultima vez*
> *Vesame, vesame mucho*
> *Que tengo miedo pederte, pederte otra vez*
> *Each time I cling to your kiss, I feel moments divine!*

"For my Nippon boy friend, a haunting song." Fides sang:

> *Sakura, sakura, yayo ino, sorawa*
> *Miwatasu, kagiri, kasumika, kumoka*
> *Nio-izu izuru, izaya, izaya, mini, yukan.*

"*Gome nasai*," Fides intoned. "I'm sorry, I made you cry. Now my favorite, it's about me," and she sang:

> *Ang Dalagang Pilipina,*
> *Parang tala sa umaga*
> *Kung tanawin ay nakaliligaya.*

Ceres and Tem joined the chorus:

> *Malinis ang puso, maging sa pag-big*
> *May tibay at lakas ang loob.*

But Mario interrupted them with the song:

> *"I'm dreaming of a white Christmas . . . "*

"Yeah, like Laurel," interrupted Ruben, "dreaming of a white Christmas too, but in Japan. He said after being released by his colleagues in the Philippine government: 'All Filipinos were collaborators, others may like the United States, but I don't. It was the duty of America to defend her sovereignty here and when she couldn't, why should Filipinos defend it? We have done our duty.' "

"Yeah, but whose sovereignty did he defend? The Philippines?" asked Mario. "Where was he when the Japs were bayonetting our babies and women in Vito Cruz, in St. Scho, in La Salle, everywhere? Hah? Hah?"

"In Baguio, in Japan. Why should he stay in an open city? That's why it was declared open, so you can fly away!" said Ceres.

"Corny, stupid!" said Mario.

"Really, children, you joke about everything, even of serious matters. You are like clowns, with your big mouths," said Ma.

"Yes, we are clowns, the laughing-stock of the world! After we fought the Japs, we make those who made money with our enemies, we make them our leaders, ha, ha! You're right, Ma, we are clowns!" said Ceres.

"Come, come, we have so much to do. No more time for jokes and anger. It's so easy to go to war, so hard to rebuild after the war. Look, I lost my piano, and I've sold my jewelries," said Ma.

"All?" asked Fides.

"Well, not all. I've set aside a few valuable pieces of sentimental value to me. But we have to make a real roof over our head. We cannot live in this makeshift shack forever. We need beds, cooking stoves and utensils, my piano, a million things. Begin all over again. So let's get to work!" ordered Ma.

What about the rest of the nation? They discussed that too. The Filipino people had resented the lack of American wartime support during the four years of Japanese occupation; the eleven-mile relief convoy that was promised never came until it was driving feverishly up north for the total destruction of Manila. Now that support funds were again needed and once more eagerly awaited by the Filipinos — this time for rehabilitation —these were to be withheld unless the Filipinos yielded to American wishes for parity rights, equal rights, and other political, economic, and military privileges in the country.

Salvador Araneta, co-founder of the Liga Filipina, organized to fight the Bell Trade Economic agreement and the parity constitutional amendments argued against these "parity rights" and he said, "We already had parity all these years under American sovereignty." Because of this and his other objections to American privileges, Manuel Roxas branded him as a "prophet of disaster."

"These Americans, just like the Spaniards and the Japanese, all these foreign invaders of our country — they give us something in return for something they take," said Pa.

"Like what?" asked Ruben.

"Like me — sending me to schools, but even that is another way they take. It's good I'm not completely taken." Pa laughed. "But many of our countrymen, especially our leaders, are easily taken — they become completely like the foreigner in mind and spirit, so Americanized, they even think it's bad to be pro-Filipino. To be Filipino!"

"Not me, I'm proud to be me whatever is me," said Ceres.

"Another thing, the Americans are so afraid of communism — well, not really the American people, but the government, those who run the government," Pa said.

"Why is that?" asked Ceres.

"They say the communists are bad, they want to rule the world. For me, I just want us to be left alone, to be what we want to be," Pa said.

"But what do you really want?" asked Ceres.

"Answer that yourself. You're grown-ups now. Seriously, no joking this time," said Pa.

"Money, lots of money," said Mario. "So I can buy a house, food, clothes, raise a family."

"I want books, school, learning, a creative mind," said Ruben.

"Love, love with one another, peace with justice," said Ceres.

"Music, theater, entertainment," said Fides. "I want to live so I can sing forever."

"Me, good health is all I want," said Tem.

"And you, Pa, what's it you want?" asked Ceres.

"All of that, but remember, not only for ourselves, but for all, all our people, rich and poor," said Pa.

"You, Ma?" asked Ceres.

"Like Pa and all of you, and faith in our people and in God, that's what I pray for," said Ma.

"Hey, we didn't ask Ciano," Ceres said. She called him and asked him what he wanted most in life.

"A wife," answered Ciano, without hesitation.

The threat of communism from the Soviet Union and China became more real than ever. Mao Zedong's Communist Party was winning the revolution in China. And so the Filipino leaders, elected upon the termination of the Commonwealth and the granting of independence in 1946, had to be, by all means, pro-American, anti-communist. They could be trusted, never mind if they had been wartime collaborators with Japan. This time the enemy was communism: the Soviet Union and China. Be pro-America: that was how rehabilitation funds were to be released and how the Philippines could be saved from communism.

Pa shook his head while reflecting on these historical events. His heart was seething with disillusion and utter disappointment, on the verge of hopelessness.

His cousin Jose Abad Santos, the only Filipino official who refused to collaborate and consciously chose martyrdom, was conveniently ignored by his colleagues and by some, condemned as a traitor to his class, the elite leadership. There was only one of his class, J. Antonio Araneta, brother of Salvador, who eulogized him:

"Like hundreds of others now enjoying the comforts and rewards of high office, like hundreds of others who prostrated themselves in cringing servility before the new masters, he could have chosen the way of submission. He did not. Because unlike them, he knew that to oppression there was only one answer — resistance. His life ended as he had lived it — with honor. "

"Why is that, Pa?" asked Ruben.

"Stupid! Filipinos are stupid, didn't you know?" Mario laughed. "You said they are cockroaches."

"Americans said that, not me," said Ruben.

"Well, this is only my guess. I really don't know," said Pa. "The elite Filipino leaders . . . "

"Who are they?" interrupted Ruben.

"Those in power, they know how to be in power. They believe they are the very foundation of the state; without them, there will be *gulo*, anarchy, violent agrarian and urban poor discontent. And we the people, because of our dependence on these leaders, we vote to retain them as leaders, rather than risk a violent upheaval from the restless masses in the barrios and city hovels. We are tired of war. The incredible destruction of our cities and our families left us numb. Look, you don't even want to go back to school yet," said Pa.

"Yes, we will, we will now," Ruben said.

"Seriously, no more joking. We will work and study hard," said Ceres.

"Good! See, you will see, slowly a sense of national pride and consciousness will begin to stir across this shattered land. And as we begin to pick up the pieces of our devastated lives, we will become conscious of ourselves as a nation. The people — we — will become conscious of our poorness as a nation, of our national poorness. We will become more conscious of the true meaning of nationalism and democracy in relation to the insurmountable problems we face in reconstructing our lives. That nationalism is not only for the few, for the elite leaders, it is for us, too, for all of us. That democracy is not just elections, electing our leaders, it is equitable distribution of wealth and justice for all." Pa's face was flushed now, as if he had rouged it like Ma.

"Most of all," said Ma, "we believe in the merciful kindness and ultimate wisdom of God Almighty. As long as we keep faith and do not lose hope, we will stave off rage from our hearts. I told you, it is hard to rebuild from the ashes of our worldly possessions and broken dreams, but let's get to work. We will never achieve anything if we just talk and talk. *Hala sige*, remember, *vox populi, vox Dei*.

Let's find God in everything and in the people."

"That's what the Jesuits taught us in Ateneo," said Ruben.

The family rebuilt their house in the same spot it had burned down, as so many others like them did. They went on with their lives: Pa in the hospital; Ma resuming her charities at home as a refuge of the homeless relatives and friends; the kids with their boy and girl friends and schooling.

Four years later, in 1950, Mario went to Mindanao where he said he would make a fortune. "I'll be back," he said, as he had said when he went off to war the last time. "With more money than you can count." There he met a girl and married her.

Tem, after college, married a cousin in the Bicol province. "Ma said, 'always room for one more,' so don't be surprised, I'll be back with one more," she teased.

The friendship of Ceres and Corban blossomed and they got married. Ceres finished her pre-medicine course but she was not pursuing her studies to medicine.

"What will you do with your degree?" asked Pa.

"I'm into a graduate program in education. I've been thinking, Pa. It's so easy to destroy bodies of men, to kill 'em — war, the atom bomb, and all that — but not the spirit, the thoughts, the soul, when you've got it deeply imprinted with goodness and kindness and love. I'll apply for a teaching position — I'll work with values and attitudes of children instead of their germs and toxins."

Pa lowered his eyes.

"Don't worry, Pa," Ceres continued. "I'll have a dozen children and grandchildren, and they'll fulfill your dream and Uncle John's. Dreams die hard, I know that, Pa."

"Yes, you've got something there," said Pa. "Remember, you will meet other monsters, enemies to contend with. Life is a struggle."

"My place is in the struggle," said Ceres.

Ruben did go out into the world, as the Jesuits had said, first to the University of the Philippines, and then to Harvard University in Cambridge, Massachusetts, for his Ph.D. "After history lessons, Pa, I'm going to specialize in man's relations to man, sociology.

I remember how well you related to the poorest of the poor even if you scolded them as you cut up their stomachs."

Fides became Ma's dream come true. She persistently pursued her musical career, first with Felicing Tirona at the Philippine Women's University College of Music, then with the famous Filipina opera diva Jovita Fuentes, and finally she got a scholarship at the Curtis Institute of Music in Philadelphia, Pennsylvania, the first Filipina to ever be accepted in the prestigious school.

One day Pa received a letter announcing an award to be bestowed on him for his outstanding services as a surgeon at the PGH and the U.P., symbolized by a golden scalpel and a gold medal.

Ma quickly cooked up an elaborate celebration. She sent out notices to the big family, wherever each and everyone was. She was not sure they could all come, scattered as they were all over the country and in America.

"Remember Pa, our family is really big. But I'll pray they all come."

Sure enough God heard her prayers. Pa marched up the stage with Ma, followed by their four kids: first, Ceres and Fides, followed by Mario and Ruben; then Tem and her husband; Corban and little grandchildren; Mario's wife Fely; Ruben's wife Jean; and all the nieces and nephews, cousins, household helpers, Tecla and Deling, Adela, Maria, Paquita, Dulce, Choling, Cilia, Ciano, oh, they almost filled the stage, to the thunderous applause of students and colleagues who had been with Pa throughout the long years of his services in peacetime and in war.

Ceres thought she heard Tecla down the line softly singing with a very thin voice:

> *"Singkuling my little girl,*
> *Keep your dream, my little girl,*
> *Through wind and rain and broken dream."*

It seemed Ma heard her too. She whispered to Ceres, "Tecla told me Mrs. Magill — remember her? — is sending Deling to America, to study medicine. But she'll come back here. Work here, Tecla said."

"Like Pa and Uncle John," whispered Ceres.

Pa stood from his seat, walked straight to the rostrum, and swelled himself up for a speech, not about appendicitis, tuberculosis, or cancer, but a long-winded one about Spanish, American, Japanese history with the Philippines, just like his perennial lectures with the family. Ceres wondered if the audience weren't getting bored. She looked around, from one end of the hall to the other: all eyes were on Pa, mesmerized, silent, you could hear a pin drop.

Then Pa raised the golden scalpel and gold medal he had just received, and said:

"I dedicate this to you, young people. I challenge you to commit yourselves to change our society, so that science, technology, medicine, politics, literature, radio, newspapers, art, music, education, business, engineering, all, serve the people, not just a few but all our people. By God, I know you will, you worry, too, about that little man Juan on the street, he must survive, even with a busted appendix!" He guffawed.

Pa was the easiest to laugh. The audience exploded into laughter too. Then he added as a parting shot, "As my daughter here," and he nodded to Ceres, says, "God makes you make it happen."

Ma nudged Ceres sitting beside her. "There goes Pa, clowning as ever."

"Ma, remember when it looked hopeless, you told us to cheer up?" Ceres asked.

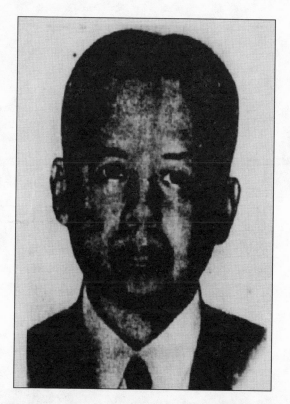

Jose Abad Santos — Chief Justice of the Supreme Court, executed by the Japanese for refusing to pledge allegiance to Japan. He was the cousin of Pa.

General Douglas MacArthur and President Manuel Quezon in Corregidor

Death March — from Mariveles, Bataan to San Fernando, Pampanga

Uncle John Santos Cuyugan and Auntie Pilar in Mintal Davao, with four of their eight daughters. Taken in 1936, years before they were all massacred.

From left to right: Rev. Victoriano Alabado, Pa, and Dr. Manuel Arguelles

Destruction of Manila and Pasay in 1945

The golden scapel and gold medal award to Pa for distinguished service

Dr. Dennis Asensio, son of Fides and Manuel Asensio, with wife Becky, and sons Michael and Ryan, in Illinois USA.

Epilogue

Mario, Ceres, Ruben and Fides, all have children and grandchildren living in the Philippines, the United States, and Canada.

Mario now lives in the old family home in Pasay, having rebuilt it for a bigger family.

After teaching education and literature at the Philippines Women's University, the Ateneo Graduate School, and the University of the Philippines, Ceres devoted her time to the women's movement struggle, and the development of Filipino children's literature. She herself writes stories for children and teenagers published in the Philippines and America. She founded the Children's Literature Association of the Philippines and established the Gawad Ceres S.C. Alabado, an award given every year for the "outstanding children's literature in the Philippines." With the support of her children she has offered the same award in Canada (with the collaboration of the National Council of Canadian Filipino Association) and in the United States (with the Philippine American Women Writers & Artists.)

Ruben, who for ten years was head of the Social Sciences Division of UNESCO in Paris, France, is now writing a book in collaboration with his second wife, Betty King, on China, the Chinese in the Philippines and America.

Fides teaches voice at the University of the Philippines. She has a weekly musical television show and has set up a Music Theater Foundation, which supports poor deserving students of music, some of whom have won first prizes in international song competitions.

Her son, Dennis Asensio, is a practicing doctor in Illinois, the same state where Pa had graduated in medicine at the University of Illinois. The golden scalpel and medal awarded to Pa, his grandfather, has passed on to Dennis until another grandchild or great grandchild claims it as a doctor.

Tem has a daughter who's a nurse, like Ma.

Deling has returned from the States and is now a practicing physician in the Philippines.

Here's a letter from Ceres' and Corban's grandson:

Dearest Lolo Corban and Lola Ceres:
In the University of the Philippines, I was accepted in Chemistry and BS Physics.
I found out I was accepted in BS Biology in Ateneo of the Society of Jesus where I was placed in the honors class of an advanced-placement course. So I confirmed my slot in the Ateneo and withdrew my other slot in the U.P.
I have enrolled for a second major in Economics. Why, you will ask. Because I intend to earn my living on business, not on my practice of medicine. I shall be a doctor for the poor, as long as there are poor people in our country. And you know what, I shall put up a scientific research foundation.

Your biologist grandson,
Jib Alabado

Cristina Alabado, whose face is the "Beautiful Dreamer" in the cover of this book is a granddaughter of Ceres and Corban. She too vows to become a doctor to serve the sick and the poor.

Pa's and Ma's dreams beam on the hearts of all whom they and their children and their children's children have touched. All that they dream and all that they are, are for God and all God's children.

"Beautiful Dreamer"

Beautiful dreamer, wake unto me
Starlight and dewdrops are waiting for thee
Sounds of the rude world heard in the day
Lulled by the moonlight have all passed away
Beautiful dreamer, queen of my song
List while I woo thee with soft melody
Gone are the cares of life's busy throng
Beautiful dreamer, wake unto me

Beautiful dreamer out on the sea
Mermaids are chanting the wild Lorelei
Over the streamlet vapors are borne
Waiting to fade at the bright coming morn
Beautiful dreamer, beam on my heart
E'en as the morn on the streamlet and sea
Then will all clouds of sorrow depart
Beautiful dreamer, wake unto me.

-Stephen Collins Foster

CERES SANTOS CUYUGAN ALABADO has children and grandchildren in the Philippines, in Canada, and in the United States. "Where the children are, I am," she says, not only for her children but for helping others too. Thus she has involved herself in civic and advocacy organization in the Philippines — Children's Literature Association of the Philippines Inc. (CLAPI), the Concerned Mothers League(CML), End Child Prostitution in Asian Tourism (ECPAT), etc; in Canada — the Philippine Women Centre; and in the United States — Philippine American Women Writers and Artists (PAWWA), Literacy Alliance (Homeless Children), etc.

For twenty years Mrs. Alabado taught education and literature in universities in the Philippines. She has written many books and stories for children and teenagers, for adult writers and for mothers, published in the Philippines, in the United States and in Canada. She was the first awardee of the Philippine Board of Books for the Young (PBBY) and the Cultural Center of the Philippines, for pioneering in the promotion and development of a national children's literature. At present she writes a column "For the Youth" in the Philippine Canadian Times of Edmonton, Alberta, Canada.

Through her children Arion, Alan, Ariel, Ana and Arrigo, she has established a GAWAD Ceres S.C. Alabado (cash award annually) for "outstanding children's literature" not only in the Philippines but also in Canada and the United States.

As a graduate of the Institute of Children's Literature of Connecticut, Ceres says: "With what I've learned from the ICL and of the American culture, I hope to help enrich children's literature here, in more ways than writing it, as my humble contribution to my adopted country which had in a long-ago past "given" so much to my father, Dr. Gervasio Santos Cuyugan."